SCIENCE MUSEUM

SCIENCE
MUSEUM
SOUVENIR GUIDE

CONTENTS

Produced exclusively for
SCMG Enterprises Ltd
by Carlton Books Ltd,
20 Mortimer Street, London W1T 3JW.

Science Museum logo © SCMG
and designs © SCMG Enterprises.
Every purchase supports the museum.
www.sciencemuseum.org.uk

Text written by Jack Challoner.

ISBN 978-1-78097-479-8

Printed in China.

Front cover: *Figure wheel on a drawing by
British computing pioneer Charles Babbage
of Difference Engine No. 2 (see page 47).*

FOREWORD

The Science Museum is the home of human ingenuity. In the 21st century, this restless institution finds itself heading the Science Museum Group, the world's biggest alliance of national science museums, which embraces five key locations – in London, Manchester, York, Bradford and Shildon – and 7.3 million objects which attract 5.1 million visits a year.

This illustrated book focuses on the Science Museum, and by selecting from the treasures displayed here our curators lay a chronological trail of clues to nation-building stories such as the industrial business partnership of steam pioneers Boulton and Watt, who are celebrated on the current £50 banknote. These pages juxtapose other seldom-seen artefacts conserved at Blythe House in London and at Wroughton near Swindon.

You will read about our hives of scholarship in collection and preservation that are constantly deriving fresh insights from our objects for new generations. We also reveal how our Learning and Outreach teams communicate their skills across the globe.

Our mission is to feed the public's appetite for making sense of the latest ideas in science, technology, engineering and medicine, how these impact on society, and how research might provide solutions to contemporary challenges. Innovation is the 21st-century way to live, as individuals and in society. The Science Museum tells an epic story about civilisation and how science has always been part of culture.

IAN BLATCHFORD
Director and Chief Executive of the Science Museum Group

HISTORY OF THE MUSEUM

The Science Museum's collections tell countless stories of human ingenuity – and show how great ideas and ingenious inventions have shaped the way we live. Just as important as making sense of the past is keeping up with what's happening today and looking forward to the future. We do that too, with intriguing interactive galleries and packed programmes of events inviting you to consider important subjects such as climate change, robotics, neuroscience and genetics. With so much for people of all ages and interests to see and do, it is no wonder that the Science Museum is one of the UK's top visitor attractions. But how long has there been a Science Museum in London? And how did it come to be?

BELOW
Queen Victoria opens the Great Exhibition of 1851. The Science Museum can trace its origins to the exhibition, which was held in the Crystal Palace, a grand purpose-built structure a few hundred metres from the Museum's current location on Exhibition Road.

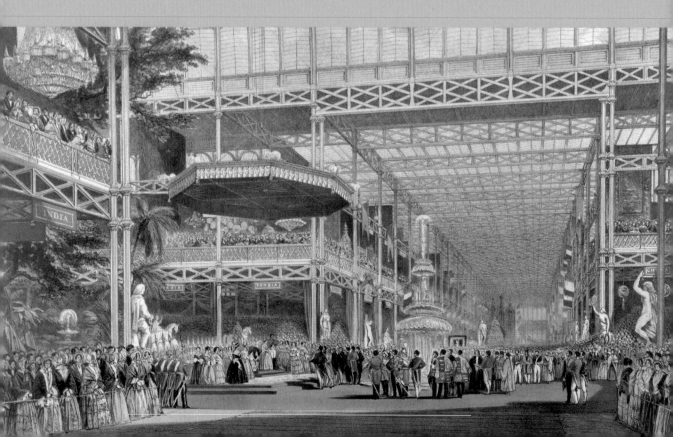

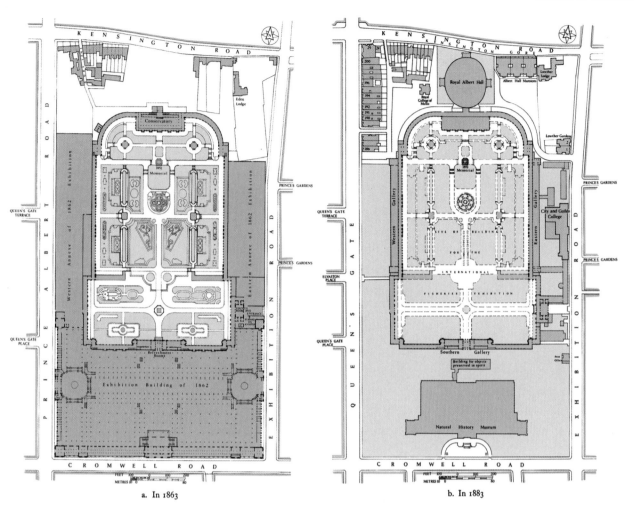

a. In 1863

b. In 1883

ORIGINS

You can trace the origins of the Science Museum back to the Great Exhibition of 1851 – or, to give it its full title: 'The Great Exhibition of the Works of Industry of all Nations'. The Great Exhibition was held in Hyde Park, less than 400 metres from the Museum's present front door. Exhibition Road, our present address, was built as a grand avenue to lead visitors up to the exhibition. Inside a magnificent steel and glass building nicknamed the Crystal Palace, exhibitors from across the world showcased the very best of industrial design and manufacture, and even raw materials – as well as the latest inventions and scientific discoveries.

The exhibition was an enormous success, and it made a huge profit. Prince Albert (husband to Queen Victoria) had been closely involved in every stage of the exhibition. Albert was keen to promote education and the advancement of British industry, so he suggested that the exhibition's profits should be used to buy land in South Kensington and build libraries, colleges, museums and a great meeting hall. That's why South Kensington now boasts so many important national cultural institutions with international reputations; the Natural History Museum, the Royal College of Art, the Royal College of Music, the Royal Albert Hall and the Victoria and Albert Museum all have their roots in Albert's grand plan.

One of the key institutions in Albert's plan was the South Kensington Museum, which opened in 1857. The South Kensington Museum displayed the same sorts

ABOVE
Plans from the Survey of London in 1863 (left) and 1883 (right) showing the block on which the Science Museum now stands. Various elements of Prince Albert's plan for South Kensington are in place in the later plan, including the Albert Hall, the Natural History Museum and the City and Guilds College.

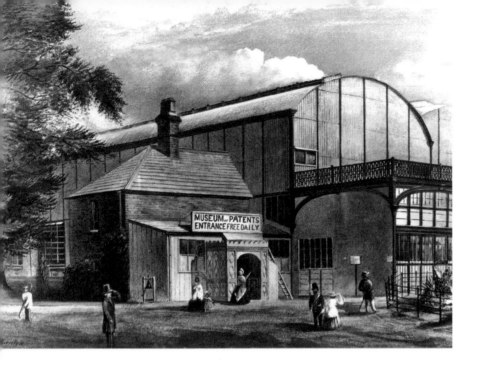

of things people had seen in the Great Exhibition: art, industrial design, machinery and even a selection of raw materials. However, science and technology hardly featured, as the museum became increasingly focused on art and design.

On the same site as the South Kensington Museum was the Patent Office Museum, where new inventions were displayed, ideally to inform and inspire budding inventors. The Patent Office Museum's director was an engineer called Bennet Woodcroft. As well as putting newly patented inventions on display, Woodcroft was determined to collect and exhibit old ones. He was fascinated by the history of technology – and he hoped that visitors might get a sense of how far science and technology had progressed and see how inventions are perfected over time. Woodcroft collected some of the things that are now among the Science Museum's most prized objects. They include William Symington's engine, which drove the first practical steam-powered boat (1788); *Puffing Billy* (1814), the world's oldest surviving locomotive; and George and Robert Stephenson's *Rocket* (1829). Woodcroft also began negotiations with the descendants of James Watt to acquire Watt's workshop, which is now on permanent display in the Science Museum.

An 1874 government report into the state of science education in Britain suggested the creation of a collection of scientific instruments – and went as far as saying that this collection, together with Woodcroft's collection and scientific objects in the South Kensington Museum, should be brought together in a single place. The result of the report was an exhibition of scientific instruments, held in 1876, across the road from the South Kensington Museum, more or less on the site where the Science Museum is today. The organisers collected objects of all shapes and sizes from right across Europe. This was a huge exhibition, with more than 20,000 objects on display – compare that to the 15,000 objects displayed in the Science Museum today. The exhibition's curator was the chemist and astronomer Sir Norman Lockyer (the co-discoverer of the element helium and founder of the scientific journal *Nature*). The general public was fascinated by the exhibition – both by the objects on display and by a series of lectures that accompanied the exhibition.

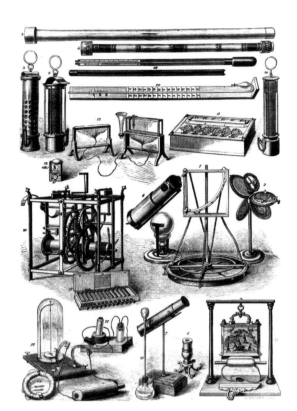

Drawings from the Illustrated London News *showing some exhibits that featured in the Special Loan Collection of Scientific Apparatus, 1876.*

Rocket, *designed by Robert Stephenson in 1829 – photographed in March 1876 outside the Southern Galleries of the South Kensington Museum.*

BIRTH OF THE SCIENCE MUSEUM

ABOVE
Construction of the East Block between May 1914 and April 1918. Innovative underfloor ducts supplied power to all parts of the building – and even compressed air to operate working models.

RIGHT
Astronomy gallery, 1926.

The success of the scientific instruments exhibition encouraged some leading scientists and industrialists – most notably, Lockyer himself – to call for the government to set up a separate science museum. Meanwhile, the South Kensington Museum continued to concentrate more and more on art and design, and less on science and technology – and those scientific or technological things it did possess were increasingly being moved across the road to the site where the 1876 scientific instruments exhibition had been. By 1893, the separation of art and science became even more defined: in that year, the South Kensington Museum had two directors – one for the arts and design collections and one for the science and technology collections.

Six years later, Queen Victoria laid a foundation stone for a new building that would house the art and design collections – and she announced that the museum would be renamed as the Victoria and Albert Museum. Ten years after that, in 1909, the secretary to the Board of Education, Robert Morant, persuaded the government to create a separate science museum at last – by cunningly pointing out that the Queen had meant the museum's new name to apply only to the art collections.

And so the Science Museum was born, and plans were made to give it its own home. Its first dedicated building, the East Block, is that part of the modern Museum that fronts on to Exhibition Road. The old buildings that had housed Woodcroft's collection and the exhibition of scientific instruments remained in use behind the new building. Work began on the East Block in 1913, but the First World War halted construction. The delay didn't put off the public, however, and visitor numbers grew while the East Block slowly gained shape; the building was finally opened, by no less than King George V, in 1928.

RIGHT
The East Block in May 1919, with a temporary façade that allowed the building to be used as government offices.

FAR LEFT
View of the East Block during an exhibition of developments in science and industry to mark the silver jubilee of King George V, in 1935.

LEFT
The sailing ships gallery on the first floor of the East Block, 1920s.

BELOW
Puffing Billy, *the world's oldest surviving steam locomotive, at the front of a line of locomotives in the rail transport gallery, on the ground floor of the East Block. Photographed in May 1924.*

COLLECT AND PRESERVE

What should a science museum collect? Apart from Woodcroft's old machines, the young Science Museum was mostly concerned with new scientific discoveries and new inventions. Then, as now, science was making huge strides forward in understanding the world, while new inventions and improvements in technology and manufacturing were rapidly transforming communication, transport, medicine, domestic life and fashion. Television, the jet engine, nuclear power, space exploration and electronic computers are just a few of the big developments that have taken place since the Museum was founded in 1909. The pace of change in the 20th century meant that 'new' technologies soon became historical objects. Partly as a result of this, and partly from a desire to educate the general public rather than just experts, Museum curators began to collect old things on purpose, and also to use their collections to illustrate the history of particular subjects.

Despite the growing collection, there was still space at the Museum to hold all the objects. Almost everything was out on display in galleries; the rest was easily accessible to visitors on request. That began to change after the Second World War. At the onset of war, nearly two-thirds of the entire collection was moved out of London, to protect it from potential damage by bombs. Some objects were put in warehouses, others underground in disused quarries, some in the outbuildings of stately homes. After the war, most objects returned to South Kensington – but it was clear that the old buildings behind the East Block were no longer suitable. As a result, some objects ended up in storage in and around London, and not on display.

ABOVE LEFT
By the early 1950s there were over 2.5 million television sets in Britain. This 1954 receiver was made by British manufacturer Murphy Radio.

ABOVE RIGHT
Atari 520 ST personal computer (1985), with a keyboard, monochrome monitor and mouse, and a floppy disk drive.

LEFT
Replica of the Huygens lander as it would have looked on touchdown on Titan, Saturn's largest moon, in 2005.

Construction of a new building, the Centre Block, began in 1949. Even with this new space, more off-site storage was needed. In 1979 the Science Museum – along with the Victoria and Albert Museum and the British Museum – began storing some small and medium-sized objects in Blythe House, a building in nearby West Kensington. Blythe House was originally used as the headquarters of the Post Office Savings Bank. Today, the Science Museum uses around 90 rooms there, storing more than 200,000 objects in carefully controlled climatic conditions; there is also a conservation laboratory and research facilities.

More than half the items held at Blythe House, and around half the objects in the Museum's entire collection, are from the Wellcome collection. This consists of objects acquired by Henry Wellcome – an American entrepreneur who co-founded the pharmaceutical business Burroughs Wellcome & Co. in 1880. Wellcome was passionate about the history of medicine and organised a team of collectors to obtain objects from all over the world. He opened a museum of medical history in London in 1913 and continued collecting until his death in 1936. The collection – along with Wellcome's vast wealth – was passed to the Wellcome Trust, which presented the unique collection to the Science Museum on permanent loan in 1976. Items from the collection were put on display in two galleries devoted to the history of medicine, which opened in 1980 and 1981.

While smaller objects not on display in the Science Museum are stored in Blythe House, larger ones are conserved and preserved in seven aircraft hangars on a former Royal Air Force airfield in Wroughton, near Swindon. The Wroughton site is also home to our library and archive collections, which house more than half a million books and documents from the history of science and technology.

ABOVE
Conservator cleaning the Pilot ACE, an important early computer (see page 71).

LEFT
In 2001 the Museum acquired the Wood printing press, which printed the Daily Mail *newspaper from 1927 until 1987. The 140-tonne press was reassembled at Wroughton.*

RIGHT
Part of a 6-metre-long Ripley scroll, from the Wellcome collection. This 18th-century scroll was rediscovered by a library assistant while preparing for an exhibition about alchemy.

THE MUSEUM TODAY

A third building was added to the Museum in 2000: the Wellcome Wing, which joins on to the back of the Centre Block. The Wellcome Wing has permanent galleries that present contemporary issues – including climate change (*Atmosphere*) and neuroscience and genetics (*Who am I?*) – and examine the cultural implications of future technology (*In Future*). Also in the Wellcome Wing is *Antenna*, a permanent gallery with frequently changing temporary exhibitions that explore the social and ethical dimensions of new developments in science and technology.

The result of more than a hundred years of development is a unique and very modern museum. If there is one thing that makes the Science Museum stand out, it is the unusual combination of historical collections and cutting-edge contemporary science communication. Nowhere is this mix more apparent than at the back of the Centre Block. Here, the Wellcome Wing meets *Making the Modern World*. Most of the Wellcome Wing galleries have very few objects and present ideas and pose important questions about contemporary issues through innovative interactive displays. *Making the Modern World*, on the other hand, has very few interactives and is a showcase for some of the Museum's most important historical artefacts.

The Wellcome Wing and *Making the Modern World* highlight another feature of the Museum – one that has become particularly important in recent years. Both these spaces depended on financial input from outside the Museum's own funds (in this case, the Heritage Lottery Fund). The Wellcome Wing also depended upon funds from the Wellcome Trust, and most of its displays and exhibitions were made possible by a variety of other funders. The Museum is still funded by central government, but running, improving and updating such a major visitor attraction – while also keeping it free – requires substantial sums of money. Continued investment is vital if the Museum is to achieve its ambitions and fulfil its roles.

What will the future hold? Many of the Museum's galleries, including *Exploring Space*, the *Energy Hall* and the *Launchpad* interactive gallery, will remain long term. But we have ambitious plans to ensure that the Museum remains fresh and relevant in a changing world, and as a result, change will always take place. New permanent galleries, such as Media Space (2013) and *Information Age* (2014) are part of those plans, and there is much more to come. So on your next visit, you may notice that some things have changed... but the Museum's main commitments – collecting, preserving, informing, inspiring and innovating – will always remain.

ABOVE
View of the Energy Hall *today, including the desk where visitors can buy tickets for the IMAX Cinema. Compare this picture with the one on page 10.*

LEFT
Atmosphere, *on the second floor.*
A huge blue glass exterior wall creates
a particular mood in the galleries of the
Wellcome Wing, while also creating a
careful balance between natural and
artificial light levels.

BELOW
The blue glow from the Wellcome
Wing spills out into Making the Modern
World, *on the ground floor of the Centre*
Block. Suspended above the gallery is a
Lockheed L10A Electra.

COMMUNICATING SCIENCE

The Science Museum is much more than a building filled with historical artefacts. From the very beginning, the Museum has been devoted to encouraging learning – as well as to exposing the public to the latest developments in science and technology. It continues to do these things today, engaging an ever-widening audience in thinking about and talking about science and technology, through dynamic and imaginative programmes of events and innovative use of interactive exhibits.

BELOW
The Museum's busy Outreach team helps us engage a wider audience. Here, a member of the team and students enjoy the Museum's stand at the Big Bang UK Young Scientists & Engineers Fair in London, 2013.

A WIDENING AUDIENCE

In the early days, the Museum was very much aimed at people who were studying science or technical subjects, or who were already knowledgeable. It did little to inspire or inform anyone else. That changed radically during the 1920s and 1930s; the Director at the time, Colonel Sir Henry George Lyons, was determined to widen the Museum's appeal. Lyons wanted to popularise science, making it more accessible; he argued that the needs of the 'ordinary visitor' – especially young people – should be placed above those of specialists. He encouraged curators to use the Museum's collections to tell stories, and to employ working models to demonstrate how some of the exhibits worked. And in 1931, after consulting with his own children, he instituted a new permanent gallery – the first of its kind anywhere in the world. The *Children's Gallery* explained scientific principles through working models, and included intriguing dioramas that illustrated scenes from the history of technology.

With buttons to press, handles to turn and ropes to pull, the *Children's Gallery* was a big hit, and it remained hugely popular until it closed in 1993. During the rest of the 1930s, the Museum introduced new ways of explaining the principles of science and technology, and of interpreting the collections, including films and audio guides. From the 1950s onwards, the Museum began showing educational films and holding public lectures in its Lecture Theatre. The Museum became a firm family favourite, providing people with happy memories of the experiences they had there, and ensuring that children would later return as adults with their own families. In the late 1950s, the Museum also began taking seriously its role in formal education, helping teachers to ensure they made the most of their visits. The Museum remains extremely popular with school groups – in fact we welcome more booked educational visitors than any other museum in the UK.

ABOVE
Photographed in 1963, this young girl learns how lifts work, thanks to an interactive working model in the Children's Gallery.

BELOW
Children learning by doing, at the pulley blocks exhibit in the Children's Gallery, *1963.*

LAUNCHPAD AND BEYOND

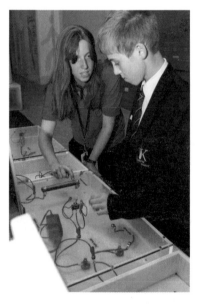

The *Children's Gallery* had a major influence on the American physicist Frank Oppenheimer when he spent time living in London in the mid 1960s. On his return to the USA, Oppenheimer created the world's first modern interactive science centre, the Exploratorium, which opened in 1969. The Exploratorium also employed staff to engage the visitors with the exhibits and to perform science shows – something that Oppenheimer had seen in other European museums. The Exploratorium was extremely popular, and its success soon spawned similar centres around the world. In 1981 the Science Museum played host to a travelling exhibition from one of them: the Ontario Science Centre. The exhibition was a big hit, and the Museum decided to create its own interactive science centre, *Launchpad*, which opened in 1986. As in other science centres, members of staff were on hand to encourage visitors of all ages to interact with the exhibits, to ask and answer questions and to share their enthusiasm for science. The *Launchpad* staff – renamed 'Explainers' in 1990 – also performed science shows for school groups during the week, and for general visitors during weekends and school holidays, and really brought science to life.

In 2007, *Launchpad* moved to its current home, on the third floor, and benefited from a major makeover. It now welcomes more than a million visitors each year. Explainers are still very much on hand, providing friendly faces, enthusiasm and positive role models for young would-be scientists and inventors. Explainers perform spectacular daily science shows on a wide range of scientific topics, both in *Launchpad* and in the Lecture Theatre, including the ever-popular Bubbles show. Each year, nearly 400,000 visitors take part in these shows. Our Learning teams also deliver shows to more than 100,000 people each year beyond the Museum's walls – in schools, festivals, libraries and hospitals, as well as making the odd appearance on television.

LEFT
Light Table is an exhibit in the Light zone, where you can experiment with mirrors, lenses, prisms and coloured filters.

BELOW LEFT
At the exhibit called Lens Line-Up, in the Light zone, you can investigate optics by moving up to four large lenses in a row.

BELOW RIGHT
Echo Tube, in the Sound zone, allows you to hear the echo of your voice. Closing a shutter effectively divides the 35-metre-long tube in half, and the echo returns in half the time.

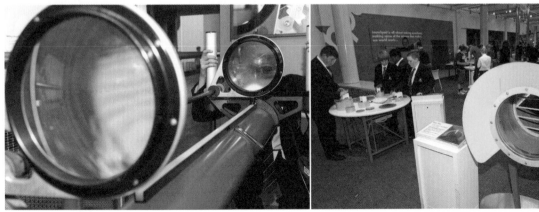

ABOVE RIGHT
Digital exhibits, inside the Museum and online, help to interpret static objects such as 'Old Bess', the oldest surviving Boulton and Watt steam engine, which stands proudly in the Energy Hall.

The spirit of the *Children's Gallery* and *Launchpad* has spread: today, the Museum boasts several partly or wholly interactive galleries, and interactive exhibits enhance the opportunities for learning in a number of other galleries. *The Garden*, in the basement, is a *Launchpad*-style space where three- to six-year-olds can interact with water, structures, light and sound. Exhibit labels give simple explanations, but the focus is very much on the experiences children have there. *The Secret Life of the Home*, also in the basement, has many working models, while *Challenge of Materials*, on the first floor, contains lots of interactive exhibits that encourage you to explore and experience the properties of a range of materials.

The rise of digital technology has enabled exhibition designers to incorporate more interactivity into other galleries, in a variety of ways. For example, *Energy*, on the second floor, uses digital interactive exhibits to explain the concept of energy, and to raise important questions about how we harness and use it. We also use interactive digital displays to help reveal the workings, the importance and the stories of some of the otherwise static exhibits, including many of the large steam engines in the *Energy Hall* and many of the objects in *Making the Modern World*. Digital technology also enables us to update content regularly, and in some cases to synchronise what appears in the Museum with what is published online. Henry Lyons would be amazed.

ABOVE
Challenge of Materials, *on the first floor, contains a mixture of objects and hands-on interactives, providing an immersive look at the science and history of materials.*

LEFT
The Secret Life of the Home, *in the basement, helps you to understand how everyday technologies work – from CD players to flushing toilets.*

MORE THAN EXPLAINING

Our science shows, interactive galleries and the interactive digital exhibits that accompany Museum objects are aimed at giving clear explanations of the principles or the history of science and technology. But they also aim to inspire curiosity, and to encourage visitors to think for themselves. Throughout the Museum, we also explore contemporary scientific research, and encourage visitors to think about and engage in dialogue about some of the social and ethical issues it raises. Nowhere is this more evident than in the Wellcome Wing – and in particular in *Antenna*, on the Wellcome Wing's ground floor.

Antenna, the most regularly updated science news gallery in the world, explores ethical issues behind cutting-edge scientific research. Content on the gallery changes daily, exhibits are changed every month, and the more in-depth feature exhibition, once a year. The highly trained science communicators behind the gallery translate complex science into accessible content, and carry out relevant interviews with experts representing different points of view, provoking emotional responses to important ethical issues surrounding the latest research. Importantly, both the gallery and the website offer you the opportunity to share your thoughts and feelings about the issues presented.

LEFT
Dr Andrew Spence of the Royal Veterinary College, London, explains his research into insect locomotion as part of the Cockroach Robot event during the Robotville Festival (2011).

BELOW
Students visiting Who am I? examine a reconstruction of one of the earliest Europeans. The model was based on 35,000-year-old skull fragments found in Romania.

TOP
Visitors to Atmosphere are immersed in an innovative virtual world, with oceans, land and atmosphere. The gallery's principal content contributor was the Met Office.

ABOVE
The Who am I? gallery uses an engaging combination of interactives and objects to explore how your brain, genes and body make you unique.

RIGHT
Visitors to the Live Science Event in Who am I? explore three-dimensional pictures of their faces, as part of research into facial structure by scientists at Great Ormond Street Hospital.

On the first floor, *Who am I?* – a perfect mix of interactives and objects – considers how the latest discoveries in genetics and neuroscience are redefining how we understand ourselves. On the second floor, *Atmosphere* invites visitors to investigate climate science, reports on the latest climate news and prompts visitors to dig deeper into the important issue of climate change. Interactive digital exhibits in *Atmosphere* encourage visitors to explore scales of time and space, to investigate the implications of climate change. There are objects too – including a real Antarctic ice core, tree rings and scientists' instruments – reminding us of the real observations on which climate science is based. *In Future*, on the third floor, contains exciting interactive 'games' that bring visitors together and ask them to consider the impact that upcoming technologies might have on them and on future generations.

We also encourage visitors to think about the nature and practice of science itself. For example, *Pattern Pod*, on the ground floor of the Wellcome Wing, invites under-8s to explore how identifying patterns makes it easier to make predictions and to understand the nature of things; recognising and studying patterns is a crucial part of scientists' work. In Antenna Live events, typically held during school holidays, visitors can meet working scientists, to hear about and ask about how they carry out their work. You can even be the subject of real scientific experiments, in Live Science on the first floor, where scientists take up residence for a few months. The resident researchers benefit by gaining access to a wide demographic, and are always surprised at how quickly they gather data – information that will contribute to real scientific papers. And they are always glad of the chance to hone their own communication skills.

BELOW
'Will you be the first person to live for 1000 years?' asks this exhibit, featuring a model of the DNA double helix, in Who am I?

BRINGING IT ALL TOGETHER

All the different approaches to engaging visitors in science and technology feature in our ambitious out-of-hours events: Science Nights and Science Museum Lates. Science Nights are themed science sleepovers, in which 7- to 13-year-olds enjoy an evening of science shows, workshops, an IMAX film, storytelling and gallery tours, before sleeping in the Museum then waking to a healthy breakfast and more events. We stage around ten Science Nights every year, creating experiences that children will never forget. Science Museum Lates, held on the last Wednesday of every month (except December), are themed evenings for adults only. A licensed bar and DJs set the scene, while visitors enjoy talks and discussions from leading scientists and experts, hands-on activities – and a chance to enjoy *Launchpad* child-free! Lates attract more than 35,000 young adults each year, reinforcing the idea that the Museum is not just for children. Special events such as these help us stay fresh and current in a changing world, and allow us to present science in a direct and engaging way.

We have made it our mission to help our visitors make sense of the science that shapes our lives. The Science Museum is neither a classroom nor a textbook, but we pull out all the stops to make sure that *real* learning takes place. We've forged relationships with scientists around the world, and with the leading science journals *Science* and *Nature*, so that we can develop meaningful exhibits before reporting embargoes are lifted and have them on gallery as the news breaks. And, of course, we always make sure we've got the most important ingredient right: people. In addition to the Explainers, visiting scientists, actors and workshop facilitators working directly with visitors, there are teams of people behind the scenes researching, planning and preparing new galleries, exhibitions and events. Our curators play a vital role, ensuring that the collections remain relevant and are well looked after – and lending their expertise to the development of new galleries and exhibitions. And all the time our world-leading Audience Research and Advocacy group is increasing our understanding of how people learn in museums and feeding the results into the planning of new exhibits, galleries and events.

The friendly, open and engaging character we have developed over the years, along with our unique collections, makes us a world leader in communicating science to people of all ages and from all backgrounds. And we are determined to continually review and improve what we do, widen our audience still further and offer ever more challenging content. Getting people involved in science and technology is crucial to our nation's future prosperity – and the Science Museum is the perfect place to do it. You can learn about science and technology from books and the internet, but the Science Museum offers a unique opportunity to experience *real* objects with *real* importance and to interact with *real* people with a *real* passion for science.

ABOVE
A student constructing a working model of a Mars rover, as part of the launch party for Science Boxes, resource kits filled with themed science activities aimed at science and engineering clubs.

RIGHT
Secondary school students investigating the strange properties of liquid nitrogen as part of The Super Cool Show, hosted in their school by our Outreach team.

RIGHT

A Museum visitor taking part in Antenna Live: Champion Rowers – an interactive event staged by Team GB rowers Heather Stanning and Moe Sbihi, with coaches from the GB Rowing Team and the London Youth Rowing Team.

BELOW

The world's first soft-bodied robot being showcased at an Antenna half-term event. The lifelike 'Octobot' can sense its surroundings and can grab and squeeze objects – and may one day be developed into a robot that can repair underwater pipelines or even carry out marine search and rescue.

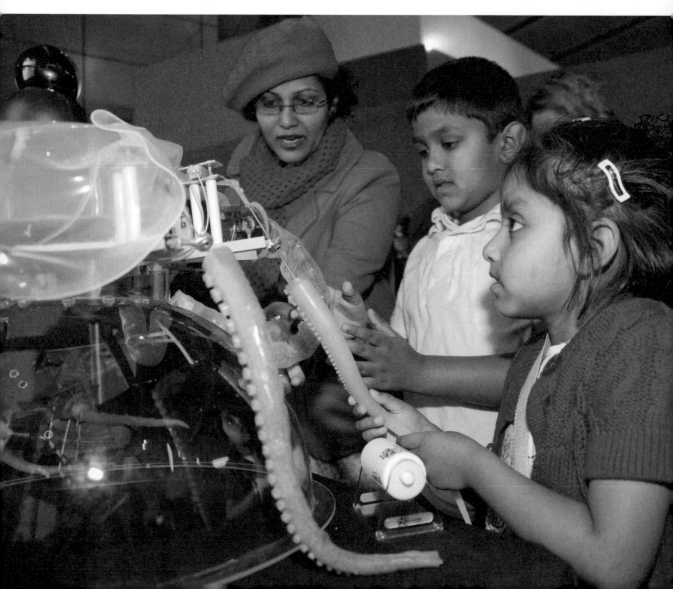

THE SCIENCE MUSEUM ONLINE

The Museum's website extends our reach to millions of people. Our web pages present information about the Museum and its collections, exhibitions and events, but also about science and technology in general. The online team have also worked closely with games designers to create popular online games that tie in to some of our galleries; *Launchball* brings *Launchpad* online, enabling gamers to interact with various mechanical and electrical devices; *Futurecade*, related to *In Future*, engages gamers in scenarios involving future technologies; in *Thingdom*, related to *Who am I?*, users mate virtual creatures, applying the rules of genetics; in *Rizk*, related to *Atmosphere*, players manage risk on an alien world.

BELOW

The Science Museum website provides more ways for us to communicate science – including online games linked to some of our galleries – as well as informing you of what's on. Find the website at www.sciencemuseum.org. uk. See also www.ingenious.org.uk and www.makingthemodernworld.org.uk.

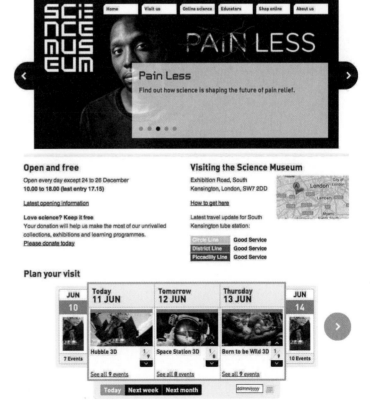

TREASURES OF THE SCIENCE MUSEUM

From stone tools to genetically engineered sheep; from mud-brick houses to personal computers... In the pages that follow we present more than a hundred objects from our vast collections, arranged in chronological order to illustrate how humans' ability to wonder, discover and create has shaped our world and developed our understanding of it.

BELOW
Remains of a remarkable 6th-century Byzantine sundial-calendar, which displayed the day and date and phases of the Moon.
Measuring Time, 1983-1393

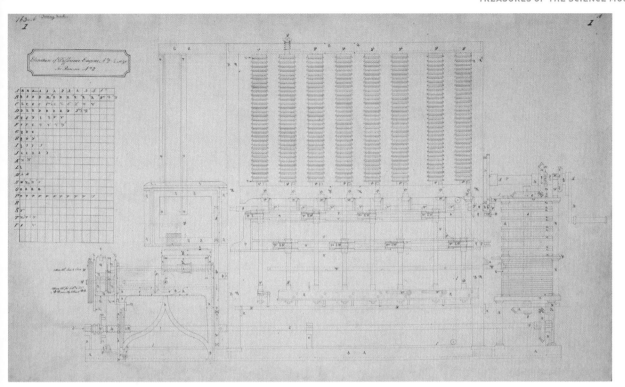

ABOVE
*Drawing of Difference Engine No. 2
(see page 47) by its inventor Charles
Babbage – one of hundreds of thousands
of important historical books, manuscripts
and documents held in the Museum's
library and archive collections.*

LEFT
*Mount Vesuvius erupting, 1767, from an
exceptional copy of Sir William Hamilton's
Campi Phlegraei, published in 1776, which
is also held in the Museum's library and
archive collections.*

There are around 15,000 objects on display in the Museum at any one time,
and we hold more than 220,000 altogether. Every one of them is a testament
to human ingenuity. To make the small sample in this section representative
of the kinds of things we have collected and continue to collect, we have
included objects relating to pure science, engineering, astronomy, scientific
demonstrations, timekeeping, transport, communications and everyday life.
There are also a lot of objects from the history of medicine; most of these are
from the important Wellcome collection (see page 15). As you follow the timeline,
you will notice that ten of the objects have whole pages devoted to them, and
longer explanations. These are among our most popular and important exhibits.

Most of the objects in this section are on display in the Museum, but we have also
included objects that are in our stores at Blythe House and Wroughton. At the
end of each entry we list the object's location in a gallery or storage facility and
its object number, which enables you to find out more about it online.

8500 BCE
STONE AGE FLINT-BLADE HAND TOOL

*The objects on these first two pages
highlight some of the most important
early technologies which radically
changed people's way of life: tools,
shelter, metalworking, lighting, pottery
and glass-making. These advances
were largely the result of people living
settled lives, rather than hunting and
gathering. Being settled certainly gave
Neolithic ('new stone age') flint-knappers
a chance to take more pride in their work
than their Palaeolithic ('old stone age')
counterparts: notice the polished surface
around the blade (at the top).*

Blythe House store, 1981-2120/3

5000 BCE
MUD-BRICK HOUSE

*No, we don't have a full-size 7000-
year-old mud-brick house in our
collection. This is a model, based
on a house that was excavated in
Jericho, one of the world's first
cities. The bricks were made of
straw with a binder of fine mud, left
out in hot sun to harden. In fact, this
is a smart combination of materials
– an early 'composite'.*

Wroughton stores, 1979-616

2000 BCE
REVERSIBLE
AXE ON ADZE

*This exquisite adze, from Papua
New Guinea, was used for working
wood. It has the greenstone head
embedded in a crosspiece; if the
head were embedded in the handle,
it would be an axe. Axes chop and
cut wood, while adzes shape and
smooth it.*

Blythe House store, 1926-102

300 CE
ROMAN DOUBLE UNGUENT BOTTLE

The Romans were not the first to make glass, but they took glass-making and glassware to a whole new level: they were the first to make clear glass, and to perfect glass-blowing. This beautiful pair of bottles held unguent (an oily ointment used to soothe the skin).
On loan to Natural History Museum, A628655

100 CE
SMALL POTTERY LAMP

Vegetable or mineral oil soaks into the small textile wick of this lamp, vaporises and ignites, feeding the small flame. Lamps like this were convenient, portable light sources – a crucial technological advance. There is another important innovation here: pottery. Potters developed skills to find the right clays, form them and fire them. In this case the results were so durable they have lasted 2000 years.
Blythe House store, 1953-476/2

c.400 BCE
BRONZE SURGICAL KNIVES

These knives were used in ancient Egypt to remove organs during mummification. Bronze tools were sharper than stone, could be worked more easily and were more durable. The Egyptians learned about bronze from the Sumerians, in Mesopotamia (modern-day Iraq), who also invented the wheel.
The Science and Art of Medicine, A634903, A634906

c.1000
ISLAMIC SUBLIMATION AND ALEMBIC APPARATUS

The science of chemistry only really began in the 18th century – but people had been using many of the techniques modern chemists use for hundreds of years. These glass vessels, made in Persia around 1000, were used for separating mixtures, by distillation and sublimation.

Blythe House store, 1978-219/220

1392
WELLS CATHEDRAL CLOCK

The Wells Cathedral clock is the third-oldest surviving clock in the world; its beautifully decorated face is still in situ in the cathedral. The mechanism is driven by a falling weight on a rope that is wound up every morning, so that it can tick away all day in the Measuring Time gallery. Mechanical timekeeping was a crucial new technology that spread around Europe at this time. Remarkably, no-one knows the names of the clock's inventors or its first builders.

Measuring Time, 1884-77

1560s
GENOESE MEDICINE CHEST

There are 126 bottles and pots for medicines in this grand chest, which was made for Vincenzo Giustiniani, who ruled the island of Chios in the Aegean Sea. Some of the bottles still appear to have their 16th-century contents, including compounds such as rhubarb powder, juniper water and mustard oil.

Science and Art of Medicine, A641515

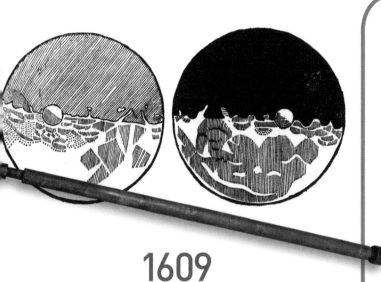

1642
GALILEO PENDULUM

19TH-CENTURY MODEL

Galileo discovered that the time of a pendulum's swing depends on its length, not on the weight of the bob – and realised that pendulums could be used to increase the accuracy of mechanical clocks. Galileo's biographer made a drawing of the idea; this 19th-century model is based on that drawing.

Blythe House store, 1883-29

1609
GALILEO'S TELESCOPE

1923 REPLICA

Galileo Galilei made ground-breaking astronomical observations using a telescope – observations that helped to confirm the then controversial idea that Earth orbits the Sun. He published drawings and explanations of his observations in Sidereus Nuncius *('Starry Messenger'). This replica of Galileo's telescope was specially made for the Science Museum in 1923.*

Exploring Space, 1923-667

1582
JOHN DEE'S CRYSTAL

English astrologer and mathematician John Dee claimed he was given this crystal by the angel Uriel. He believed it possessed magic powers that could cure a range of diseases. Later, the alchemist Nicholas Culpeper acquired it; he stopped using it because, he claimed, a demonic ghost had burst forth from it.

Loaned to touring exhibition, 'Curiosity: Art & the Pleasures of Knowing', A127915

1650
ANATOMICAL MODELS

*The study of human anatomy began to thrive
in the 16th and 17th centuries. A new scientific
spirit was emerging, and printed works were
increasing the spread of medical ideas.
Physicians began to challenge accepted wisdom
about the internal arrangement and workings
of the human body. These beautiful wooden
models were probably used as teaching aids.
The one on the right is a pregnant female;
a foetus can be seen inside her uterus.*

The Science and Art of Medicine, A79252

c.1650
ACUPUNCTURE MODEL

*At around the same time as those wooden
anatomical models were being made in
Europe, followers of acupuncture in China
made this wooden figure – also probably
a teaching aid – which shows supposed
channels through which life force, or 'qi',
flows around the body. The model stands
nearly a metre tall.*

The Science and Art of Medicine, A604024

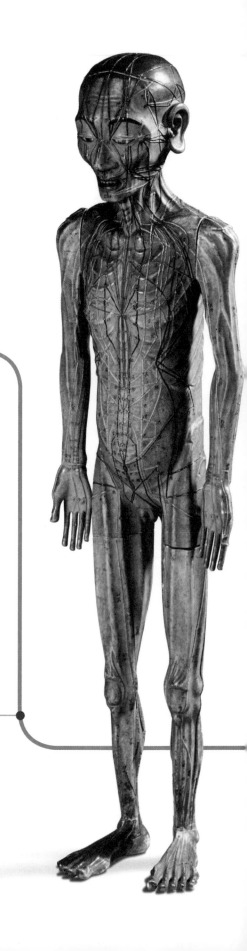

1666
ASTROLABE
BY JAMAL AL-DIN

In the 17th century, Lahore (now in Pakistan) was a great place to be if you were an astrolabe-maker. This astrolabe, 25 cm (10 inches) in diameter, was made there by Jamal al-Din, a member of a prominent family of astrolabe-makers. The astrolabe is an ancient invention that was later improved upon by Islamic scholars. People used it for a variety of functions, such as finding the time, predicting the positions of the Sun and stars – and, in the Islamic world, for determining the direction for prayer (the qibla).
Blythe House store, 1985-2077

1657
SALOMON COSTER
PENDULUM CLOCK

Dutch scientist Christiaan Huygens continued Galileo's research into pendulums (see page 37), and invented a practical pendulum clock mechanism in 1656. He licensed clockmaker Salomon Coster to make clocks based on his design – and this is one of only seven of Coster's pendulum clocks still in existence. Pendulum clocks were revolutionary: they improved timekeeping accuracy from a few minutes to a few seconds per day. Many old clocks across Europe – including the Wells Cathedral clock (page 36) – were rebuilt with pendulums.
Measuring Time, 1980-108

c.1666
SAMUEL MORLAND'S CALCULATING MACHINE

French mathematician Blaise Pascal made the first working mechanical calculator in 1642, and several mathematicians and inventors attempted to emulate or improve on his design. Morland's device, shown here, could add, subtract, multiply and divide; the wheels were operated by a steel pin that was stored in the slot in the machine's lid. Morland also invented a megaphone – or, as he called it, the 'Tuba Stentorophonica' – and a water pump for spraying water to put out fires.

Mathematics, 1876-538

1660s
ROBERT HOOKE'S MICROSCOPE

1920s REPLICA

Robert Hooke's bestseller Micrographia, *published in 1665, presented intriguing views of everyday objects, with details too small to be seen with the naked eye. This 1920s replica of one of the microscopes Hooke used while writing* Micrographia *is faithful to Hooke's description and drawing contained in the book. The drawing of a head louse clinging to a human hair (below) is reproduced from Hooke's book.*

Blythe House store, 1927-437

1769
RICHARD ARKWRIGHT'S
PROTOTYPE SPINNING MACHINE

Richard Arkwright patented this prototype horse-powered cotton spinning machine in 1769. When scaled up, powered by water wheels rather than horses and licensed for use in mills across northern England, it enabled spinning to become a factory process and so played a key role in the Industrial Revolution. A lengthy legal battle in the 1780s established that Arkwright had borrowed most of his ideas from others. His patent was cancelled, and the technology became available to use without licence.

Making the Modern World, 1860-4

1761
'NEW UNIVERSAL' SILVER
MICROSCOPE BY GEORGE ADAMS

In 1927 the Museum acquired on long-term loan a collection of 18th-century apparatus designed to demonstrate the new discoveries scientists had been making. You can see part of it in Science in the 18th Century, on the third floor. Some of the objects belonged to the lecturer Stephen Demainbray, who travelled the country during the 1750s. The rest of the collection was used to teach science to the royal family, including this exquisite silver microscope made by George Adams, instrument-maker to King George III.

Science in the 18th Century, 1949-116

1700s
ITALIAN ENEMA JAR

This tin-glazed jug is an albarello – an earthenware vessel used by apothecaries to store medicines. It was probably made in the Italian town of Deruta, renowned for its majolica pottery. Tin glazing produces bright colours and white backgrounds that make for attractive decoration; the rather alarming decoration on this albarello shows a nurse administering an enema.

The Science and Art of Medicine, A643287

TRUE- AND FALSE-COLOUR IMAGES OF THE PLANET URANUS,
TAKEN BY NASA'S VOYAGER 2 IN 1986.

c. 1790
WILLIAM HERSCHEL'S TELESCOPE

Hanover-born English astronomer William Herschel made this 2.14-metre-long (7-foot) telescope for his sister Caroline, who was also a keen and accomplished astronomer. It is very similar to the one Herschel was using when he discovered the planet Uranus in March 1781 – the first planet discovered using a telescope. (Mercury, Venus, Mars, Jupiter and Saturn were all known in ancient times, because they are visible to the naked eye.) A few years later, Herschel built a much larger telescope, with a tube more than 12 metres (40 feet) long. The original 500-kg (1025-lb) mirror of that telescope is also on display in Making the Modern World.

Making the Modern World, 1908-160

WILLIAM HERSCHEL
IN THE 1780s.

1790
GEORGE MARGETTS'
ASTRONOMICAL WATCH

A miniature version of the kind of large astronomical clocks typically installed in churches across Europe, this exquisite watch does more than tell the time. It shows the phase of the Moon and the position of the Sun among the constellations of the zodiac. It also shows which constellations will be visible above the horizon at night, gives the tide times at ports around Britain's coastline, and could even predict lunar and solar eclipses.

Measuring Time, 1963-165

1791
FRANCIS THOMPSON'S
ATMOSPHERIC ENGINE

Huge beam engines like this first pumped water out of coal mines in the 1710s. Francis Thompson built this one at Oakerthorpe Colliery, Derbyshire, and it worked from 1791 until 1918, when it was brought to the Science Museum. It's an 'atmospheric engine' because atmospheric pressure pushed the piston down with enormous force after steam condensing inside the cylinder left behind a partial vacuum.

Energy Hall, 1920-124

1790s
EDWARD JENNER'S
VACCINATION INSTRUMENTS

Pioneer of vaccination Edward Jenner used lancets like these to insert pus, from a milkmaid suffering from cowpox, into the arm of a healthy 8-year-old boy. Several days later, he proved that the boy was immune to smallpox, a much more serious disease which killed hundreds of thousands of people around the world until it was eradicated in 1979.

Making the Modern World, A647698

1820
RENÉ LAENNEC'S STETHOSCOPE

In 1816, French doctor René Laennec listened to a young woman's heart through a tube of rolled-up paper to avoid the embarrassment and impropriety of putting his ear to the woman's chest. He called his invention the stethoscope (from the Greek word for chest, stethos), and went on to make wooden versions of it like this early example. The familiar binaural stethoscope came into use in the 1840s.
Making the Modern World, A106078

c.1814
VOLTAIC PILE

REPLICA

Italian scientist Alessandro Volta invented the battery in 1800. This column of zinc and copper discs separated by cardboard discs soaked in salt solution is a faithful (1930) copy of a 'voltaic pile' battery that Volta made and gave to English scientist Michael Faraday. The availability of a steady supply of electric current made possible a host of key discoveries during the 19th century – including electromagnetic induction and several new chemical elements.
Blythe House store, 1930-728

1800s
WOODEN FIGURE OF SAINT APOLLONIA

The Wellcome Collection (see page 15) contains more than 100,000 objects relating to the history of medicine – including many statues of healing saints. Many Christians believed that praying to saints could grant cures for particular conditions. The statues depicted how a particular saint had been martyred, which influenced what kind of cure they were associated with. This rather gruesome example shows Apollonia (3rd century CE), the patron saint of toothache, having her teeth forcibly removed.
Blythe House store, A156017

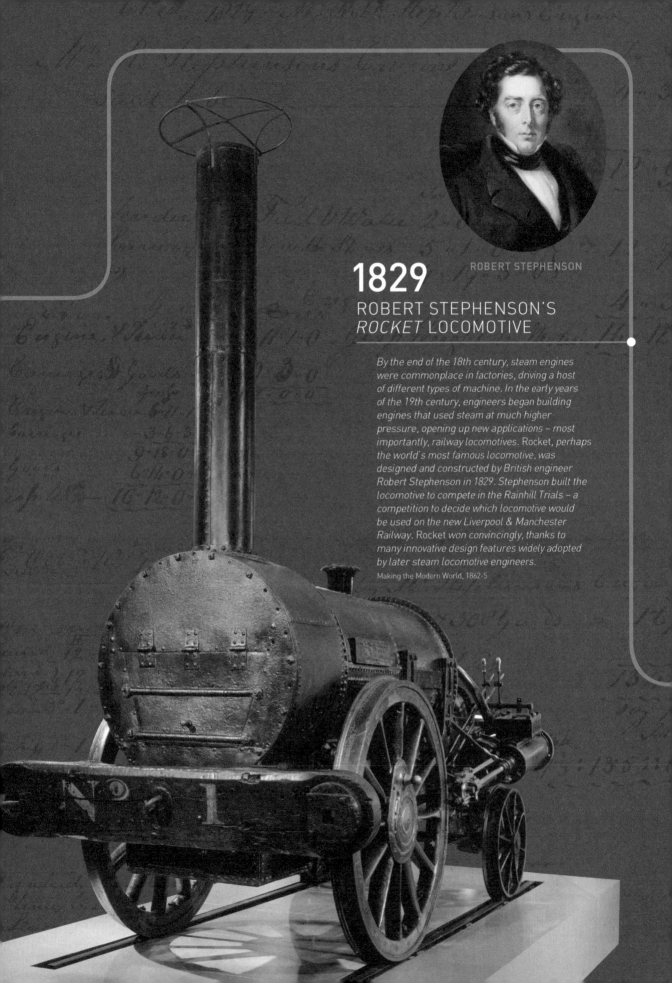

ROBERT STEPHENSON

1829
ROBERT STEPHENSON'S
ROCKET LOCOMOTIVE

By the end of the 18th century, steam engines were commonplace in factories, driving a host of different types of machine. In the early years of the 19th century, engineers began building engines that used steam at much higher pressure, opening up new applications – most importantly, railway locomotives. Rocket, perhaps the world's most famous locomotive, was designed and constructed by British engineer Robert Stephenson in 1829. Stephenson built the locomotive to compete in the Rainhill Trials – a competition to decide which locomotive would be used on the new Liverpool & Manchester Railway. Rocket won convincingly, thanks to many innovative design features widely adopted by later steam locomotive engineers.

Making the Modern World, 1862-5

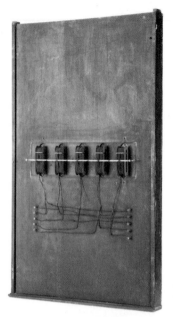

1837
COOKE AND WHEATSTONE FIVE-NEEDLE TELEGRAPH

At the same time as people were taking their first train journeys, or having their tonsils sliced off by a guillotine, a communications revolution was brewing. British pair William Cooke and Charles Wheatstone were behind the world's first practical telegraph system, which was demonstrated in 1837. Any two of the five needles in this instrument would swing to point to letters of the alphabet.
Blythe House store, 1963-215

Electromagnetic coils make the magnetic needles move.

1830s
TONSIL GUILLOTINE

For much of the 19th century no one knew the connection between microorganisms and disease, so the only treatment for tonsillitis was removal of the tonsils. The fact that there were no general anaesthetics at the time makes this all the more terrifying. The tonsil guillotine was adapted from an instrument for removing the uvula (the dangly bit at the back of the mouth). It became popular in the 1830s – although this example was made in the 1870s.
The Science and Art of Medicine, A612782

1831
SET OF MINIATURE HEADS USED IN PHRENOLOGY

Swiss sculptor William Bally made these miniature heads to illustrate the classification of head shapes devised by the German physician Johann Spurzheim, a major figure in the emerging 'science' of phrenology. Phrenologists believed that the shape and size of particular areas of a person's brain determined that person's personality – influencing the shape of the skull, the lumps and bumps of which could be read.
On loan to Museum of Science & Industry, A642804

1840s

BABBAGE DIFFERENCE ENGINE NO. 2

BUILT 1991

Charles Babbage – inventor, reformer, mathematician and philosopher – designed the Difference Engine No. 2 to solve equations and print the results in the form of mathematical tables. It was one of two types of engine, difference engines and analytical engines, designed by Babbage. The Difference Engine No. 2 was not completed during his lifetime, so the Science Museum constructed a full-sized Difference Engine No. 2 in 1991 for the bicentenary of Babbage's death. Built to the original design and assembled from 4000 parts, the Difference Engine No. 2 weighs in at over 2.5 tonnes. Both this engine and the trial sections of Babbage's other machines, the Difference Engine No. 1 and the Analytical Engine, are on display at the Museum.

Computing, 1992-556

CHARLES BABBAGE

1845
JAMES JOULE'S PADDLE WHEEL

British scientist James Joule used this apparatus in his now classic paddle-wheel experiment. Falling weights turned the paddles to churn water; the churning raised the water's temperature slightly, and Joule found that the temperature rise was in direct proportion to the amount of work done by the falling weights. Joule's 'mechanical equivalent of heat' was crucial in developing the concept of energy.

Making the Modern World, 1876-492

1845
JAMES NASMYTH'S STEAM HAMMER

James Nasmyth invented the steam hammer in 1838 to forge the paddle shafts for SS Great Britain. In the end, the ship had propellers rather than paddle wheels, but Nasmyth's invention, renowned for both its power and its control, went on to play a key role in many large engineering projects. In the black-and-white photograph, taken in 1845, Nasmyth himself stands proudly by his invention.

Making the Modern World, 1933-520

MID **1800**s
ISAMBARD KINGDOM BRUNEL'S LEATHER ATTACHÉ CASE

Isambard Kingdom Brunel is one of the icons of British engineering. His many large projects were made possible by innovations such as Nasmyth's steam hammer (left) and the increased availability of steel – but especially by his vision and charisma. They include bridges, railways and stations, docks, tunnels, ships and even a prefabricated hospital that was sent to the Crimean War. The photograph above shows Brunel at Millwall during the construction of the Great Eastern *– by far the biggest ship ever built at that time.*

On loan from STEAM, 1992-7379

1846
SEWING MACHINE BY ELIAS HOWE

American inventor Elias Howe created the first practical sewing machine, in 1845. Howe's device included the main features of modern sewing machines, including an automatic feed mechanism that pushed the fabric along step by step, and a shuttle moving to and fro beneath the fabric, carrying thread that looped around thread carried by the needle pushing through the fabric from above. Howe's brother Amasa brought this example to London in 1846 to seek funding.

Making the Modern World, 1919-235

1871
FREDERICK HOLMES'S LIGHTHOUSE GENERATOR

The discovery of electromagnetism in 1820 led to the gradual introduction of electromagnets, electric motors and generators during the rest of the 19th century. This steam-driven permanent magnet generator, designed by British engineer Frederick Holmes, powered brilliant carbon arc lamps in Souter Lighthouse, Tyne and Wear, from 1871 until 1900.

Making the Modern World, 1915-295

1865
LOUIS PASTEUR'S SILKWORMS

French microbiologist Louis Pasteur played a crucial role in establishing microorganisms as one of the main causes of disease. An important early step came in the 1860s, when he identified the cause of a disease that was decimating the French silkworm industry. We have several pieces of his laboratory apparatus, as well as this string of silkworm cocoons that formed part of his investigation.

The Science and Art of Medicine, A63336

1863
BOTTLES CONTAINING MAUVEINE

British chemist William Perkin created the first synthetic dye, mauveine, while attempting to synthesise the malaria medicine quinine. Chemists quickly discovered many other synthetic dyes, which were cheaper than natural ones and came in a wide range of new colours, kick-starting chemical synthesis on an industrial scale. These samples of mauveine, from 1863, were donated to the Museum in 1947 by Perkin's daughter, Annie.

Blythe House store, 1947-115

1877
ALEXANDER GRAHAM BELL'S TELEPHONE AND TERMINAL PANEL

Another product of research into electromagnetism was the telephone. British-born inventor Alexander Graham Bell made this particular telephone to demonstrate his new technology to Queen Victoria at Osborne Cottage on the Isle of Wight in January 1878. The mouthpiece was also the earpiece, and the user had to listen and speak alternately. No-one is sure whether the demonstration actually took place.

Making the Modern World, 1967-431/2

1878–79
SWAN AND EDISON ELECTRIC LAMPS

Development of the incandescent light bulb began in the 1840s. These experimental bulbs were made by Joseph Swan (left) and Thomas Edison (right). In 1881, Swan lamps made the Savoy Theatre in London the first public building entirely illuminated by electric light. By 1882, both men were selling bulbs commercially, Edison to customers of the first public power stations in London and New York. In 1883, the two men joined forces, forming the Edison & Swan United Electric Light Company.

Making the Modern World, 1880-70

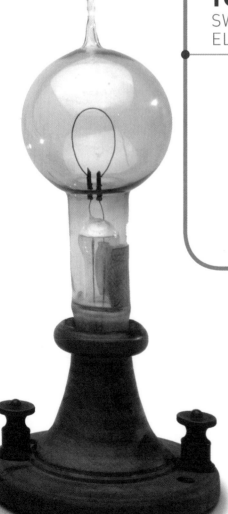

1880
SUNSHINE RECORDER

In 1853, British scholar John Campbell came up with a device that could record the hours of sunshine on a particular day. In his apparatus, a glass sphere sitting in a wooden bowl focused sunlight so that it made scorch marks in the wood; the marks became trails as the Sun moved across the sky. British physicist George Stokes improved the design in 1879, replacing the wooden bowl with a replaceable strip of paper held in a metal stand.

Blythe House store, 1909-132

1884
PARSONS ORIGINAL STEAM TURBINE

Steam engines used to power the generators in early power stations were heavy, large and relatively slow. The Charles Parsons steam turbine was a radically different design: high-pressure steam passed over shaped blades, spinning a shaft at high speed, and could turn a generator much faster and more efficiently. The shaft inside this experimental turbine rotated at 18,000 rpm. All coal- and oil-fired and nuclear power stations use steam turbines to this day.

Making the Modern World, 1890-59

1884
RUDGE 'ORDINARY' BICYCLE

Bicycles like this were popular from the 1870s. In the 1890s they became known as 'ordinaries' to distinguish them from the newfangled 'safety' bicycles. With a large front wheel, you could go further with each turn of the pedals – but riding so high up was awkward and unstable. These bicycles also had the nickname 'penny-farthing' because the large and small wheels reminded people of the relative sizes of the penny and farthing coins.

Front Concourse display, 1901-7

1894
SIR OLIVER LODGE'S COHERER

German physicist Heinrich Hertz demonstrated the existence of radio waves in 1888. The first reliable device to detect the waves was the radio-conductor, invented by French physicist Édouard Branly – in which radio waves change the electrical resistance of iron filings inside a glass tube. British physicist Oliver Lodge renamed it the coherer; in August 1894, he used this one at a meeting of the British Association, in a key demonstration of the potential of 'wireless telegraphy'.

Blythe House store, 1924-37/1

1885
ROVER 'SAFETY' BICYCLE

In the late 1870s bicycle designers were exploring new designs that would allow the rider to be closer to the ground, and that would therefore be safer. British inventor John Kemp Starley designed the first successful 'safety' bicycle in 1885. It has all the basic features of standard modern bicycles – including chain drive, which meant that both wheels could be the same size. With the introduction of the safety bicycle, cycling became enormously popular, among both men and women.

Making the Modern World, 1901-6

1894
TURBINIA ENGINE

Charles Parsons (see page 52) had
always been a keen sailor. In 1894
he fitted his 30-metre-long (100-foot)
experimental ship Turbinia with a steam
turbine, making it the fastest ship in the
world at the time and heralding a new
era of marine propulsion. Steam turbines
remained commonplace in ocean liners
until the 1960s, when diesel engines
began to supersede them.

Wroughton stores, 1927-479

1896
HMV GRAMOPHONE

The first consumer device to play back
recorded sound was the phonograph.
It played wax or tinfoil cylinders. The
gramophone, developed by German inventor
Emile Berliner in 1888, played flat discs
instead of cylinders. This model featured in
the trademark of the Gramophone Company
and its record label, HMV: a painting of a dog
called Nipper sitting next to a gramophone
listening to 'his master's voice'.

Blythe House store, 1925-461

1897
JOSEPH JOHN THOMSON'S
CATHODE-RAY TUBE

This is one of the original cathode-ray
tubes used by Joseph John ('J J') Thomson
in a series of experiments that led to the
discovery of the electron in 1897. Other
investigators had observed strange
rays emitted from cathodes (negatively
charged plates) inside glass vacuum tubes;
Thomson's experiments showed that
the rays were streams of particles. The
electron's discovery was the beginning
of an explosion in the understanding of
atomic structure, and indirectly led to the
electronics revolution of the 20th century.

'Collider exhibition', 1901-51

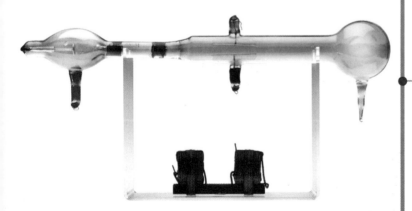

1903
MILL ENGINE

Despite the coming of power stations and the invention of powerful electric motors, steam engines remained the dominant source of power in factories in the early 20th century. This sophisticated 700-horsepower engine was installed in the Harle Syke Mill, near Burnley, Lancashire, in 1903. It powered hundreds of looms in the mill, via belts driven by the huge 20-tonne flywheel. The black-and-white photograph shows the engine in the mill just before it was dismantled in 1970. It was moved to the Museum in 1979, where it runs most days – albeit at around one-quarter of its intended speed – still powered by steam produced by a gas-fired boiler in the basement.
Energy Hall, 1971-78

1903
WRIGHT FLYER

1930s REPLICA

Many people attempted to build flying machines around the beginning of the 20th century. American brothers Wilbur and Orville Wright were the first to achieve powered sustained flight, in the Wright Flyer, in December 1903. Wilbur donated the aeroplane to the Science Museum in 1928, after a dispute with the Smithsonian Institution over priority. The original was returned to the Smithsonian in 1948 – but not before this faithful replica was made.

Flight, 1932-337

1903
POULSEN'S TELEGRAPHONE

Danish inventor Valdemar Poulsen pioneered magnetic recording in 1898. In this device, which was used as a dictation machine and answering machine, a long steel wire became magnetised as it passed close to a recording head that carried an audio signal. Although technically successful, Poulsen's system did not come into its own until electronic amplification was developed. Recording machines based on Poulsen's principle using magnetic wire or plastic tape were introduced in the 1930s.

Blythe House store, 1924-188

1904
JOHN AMBROSE FLEMING'S ORIGINAL THERMIONIC VALVE

John Ambrose Fleming's invention represents a key moment in the history of electronics. It's called a 'valve' because it only allowed electric current to flow in one direction. Connected to an antenna, it could detect radio waves in wireless telegraphy (Morse code messages via radio). Other inventors developed thermionic valves into devices that could amplify or could be used as electronic switches – so that they played a vital role in every aspect of electronics, including the first electronic computers.

Making the Modern World, 1925-814

c.1905
MR GIBSON'S PHARMACY

RECONSTRUCTION

The Gibson family opened a pharmacy in Hexham, Northumberland, in 1834. The shop's interior remained largely unchanged until it closed in 1978, its shelves still populated by a bewildering array of 'shop rounds' (glass jars that held medication). Most of the shop rounds had labels carrying the abbreviated Latin names of their contents. We acquired the entire contents and fittings of the shop in 1979, and it has been on permanent display ever since, recreated as it would have been in 1905, behind a faithful replica of the shop front.
Glimpses of Medical History

1905
DIAL TELEPHONE

In 1890, American funeral director Almon Strowger discovered that the wife of one of his competitors was a local switchboard operator – and was putting callers through to her husband and not Strowger. In response, Strowger invented an automatic exchange, through which callers could connect their own calls using push buttons or, later, a rotary dial. This telephone is from the USA; the first automatic exchange in Britain opened in 1912.

Telecommunications, 1926-1056

1905
BOOTH'S VACUUM CLEANER

British engineer Hubert Cecil Booth came up with the idea for the vacuum cleaner in 1901, after watching railway carriages being cleaned using compressed air to blow away dust and debris. Booth's brainwave was to create a machine that sucked up dirt rather than blowing it away. His early machines were large and expensive, so at first he offered vacuuming as a mobile service. Typically horse-drawn, the machines were parked outside houses and long hoses were fed through windows. This one was made for the naval academy at Osborne House on the Isle of Wight.

The Secret Life of the Home, 1958-199

1909
MECHANICAL
CASH REGISTER

In 1879, American bar owner James Ritty invented the cash register. He hoped his invention would thwart his employees' attempts at pocketing money – his first model was called 'Ritty's Incorruptible Cashier'. The National Cash Register Company was formed in Ritty's home town of Dayton, Ohio, after he sold his rights to the invention in the 1890s. This hand-crank-operated machine, made by that company, features a printer that produced paper receipts.
Making the Modern World, 1988-184

1909
SIR HIRAM MAXIM'S
'PIPE OF PEACE'
BRONCHIAL INHALER

American-born British inventor Hiram Maxim is best known for inventing a self-powered machine gun, in the 1880s. Among his many other inventions was this inhaler, intended to ease breathing, with the soothing vapours produced by a few drops of his own concoction, 'Dirigo', in warm water. His friends told him they were worried it might destroy his reputation, but good reports from users led to a surge in demand and hundreds of thousands were sold.
Making the Modern World, 1981-982/1

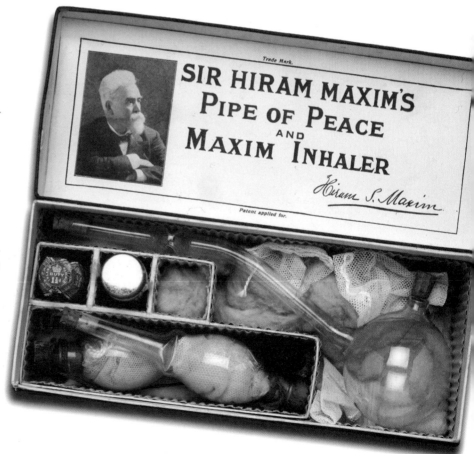

1909
LOUIS BLÉRIOT'S MONOPLANE

On 25 July 1909, French aviator Louis Blériot became the first person to fly across the English Channel. His flight took just under 40 minutes and won him a £1000 prize from the Daily Mail – equivalent to more than £50,000 today. This is the control mechanism from an almost identical Blériot XI model. The actual cross-Channel aeroplane is on permanent display at the Musée des Arts et Métiers, in Paris. The photograph shows the aeroplane shortly after it flopped down in a field just outside Dover.

Flight, 1920-33

1916
FORD MODEL T

American industrialist Henry Ford is famous for making motoring affordable for millions of people. His Model T, introduced in 1908, was enormously popular. The engine (sectioned view left) remained virtually unchanged until production ceased in 1927. To keep up with demand and reduce the car's price, Ford introduced assembly-line working. During much of the time the Model T was in production the choice of paint was limited to black because it was the fastest-drying colour.

Making the Modern World, 1997-1590

1919
VICKERS VIMY
ROLLS-ROYCE BIPLANE

*Just ten years after Blériot's flight across the
English Channel (see left), British aviators
John Alcock and Arthur Whitten Brown
claimed another Daily Mail aviation prize –
this time for £10,000 – when they crossed the
Atlantic Ocean. They crash-landed in a bog
near Clifden, Connemara, Ireland, 16 hours
after leaving Newfoundland, Canada (above
right). The Vickers Vimy aircraft they flew had
been designed as a bomber during the First
World War, and extra fuel tanks were added
for the transatlantic crossing. The replica of
the cockpit (above) is at Wroughton.*
Flight, 1959-308

ALCOCK (LEFT)
AND BROWN

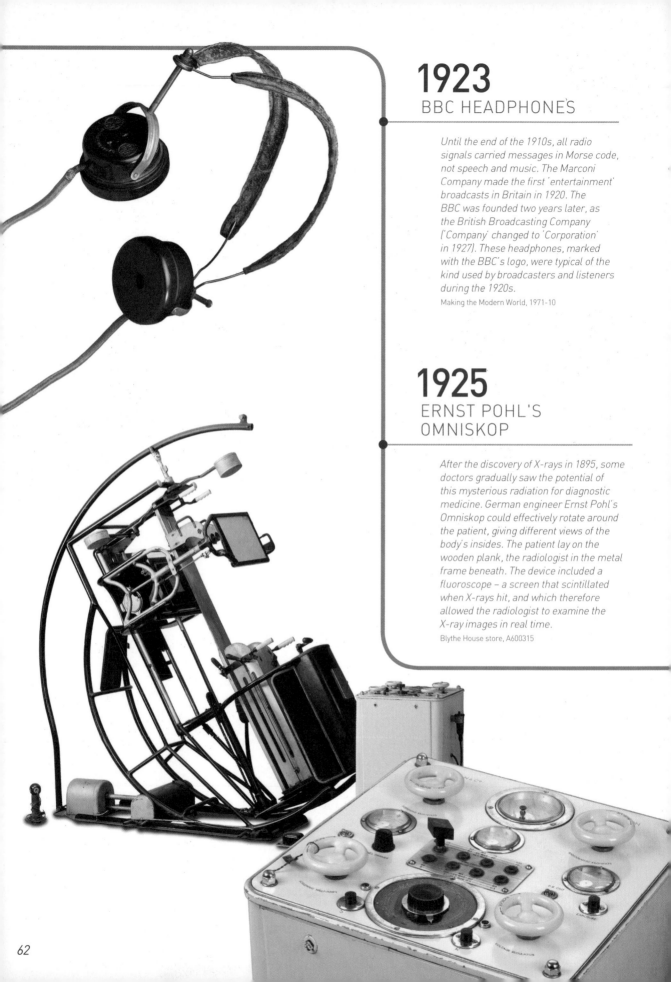

1923
BBC HEADPHONES

*Until the end of the 1910s, all radio
signals carried messages in Morse code,
not speech and music. The Marconi
Company made the first 'entertainment'
broadcasts in Britain in 1920. The
BBC was founded two years later, as
the British Broadcasting Company
('Company' changed to 'Corporation'
in 1927). These headphones, marked
with the BBC's logo, were typical of the
kind used by broadcasters and listeners
during the 1920s.*

Making the Modern World, 1971-10

1925
ERNST POHL'S
OMNISKOP

*After the discovery of X-rays in 1895, some
doctors gradually saw the potential of
this mysterious radiation for diagnostic
medicine. German engineer Ernst Pohl's
Omniskop could effectively rotate around
the patient, giving different views of the
body's insides. The patient lay on the
wooden plank, the radiologist in the metal
frame beneath. The device included a
fluoroscope – a screen that scintillated
when X-rays hit, and which therefore
allowed the radiologist to examine the
X-ray images in real time.*

Blythe House store, A600315

1928
'JASON' DE HAVILLAND GIPSY MOTH BIPLANE

British aviator Amy Johnson was born in 1903 – the same year as the Wright brothers made their first sustained flight (see page 56). She found fame in May 1930, when she flew solo from Croydon, UK, to Darwin, Australia. With 15 stops along the way, the 18,000 km (12,000-mile) journey took 20 days. The aeroplane in which she made her historic flight – a de Havilland Moth she named 'Jason', with a de Havilland Gipsy engine – is on permanent display in Flight, on the third floor. It has a wooden frame and fuselage, and was covered with fabric. Johnson had it painted bottle green with silver lettering.

Flight, 1931-27

AMY JOHNSON

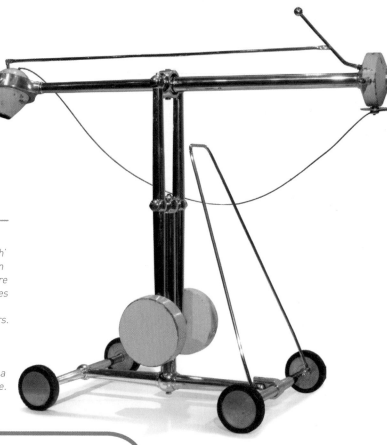

1930s
RADIUM TELETHERAPY APPARATUS

In the 1920s, the radioactive element radium was used in a wide range of 'health' products, including radium water and even radium chocolate. These products did more harm than good, but radioactive substances did prove to be beneficial when used in radiotherapy to destroy cancerous tumours. This apparatus, made at Westminster Hospital in London, exposed patients' tumours to radiation emitted by a sample of radium held in the egg-shaped unit, via a shutter released by the bicycle brake cable.
Making the Modern World, A639472

1932
RIBY TWIN-TUB WASHING MACHINE

With automatic washing machines several years away, doing the laundry would still have involved much more than just loading and pressing a few buttons for the owner of this early twin-tub machine. But it does have a connection to the gas supply – to heat the water in the tub on the right – and an electric motor to spin-dry the clothes in the tub on the left, so this washing machine did offer some convenience.
The Secret Life of the Home, 1986-686

1935
ALEXANDER FLEMING'S PENICILLIN MOULD

British biologist and pharmacologist Alexander Fleming gave this sample of the mould Penicillium notatum *to a colleague at St Mary's Hospital, London, in 1935. Seven years earlier, Fleming had discovered by chance that this species of mould produces a substance he called 'penicillin' that was found to have powerful antibiotic properties.*

Making the Modern World, 1997-731

1934
SHELVADOR ELECTRIC COMPRESSION DOMESTIC REFRIGERATOR

In the early 1930s, with a rapidly growing demand for domestic refrigeration in the USA, American entrepreneur Powel Crosley began making refrigerators. He bought the rights to a simple innovation: putting shelves inside the refrigerator door. Other manufacturers had rejected the idea, but consumers agreed with Crosley. The Shelvador became a market leader, and was the only refrigerator with shelves in the door until the patent ran out.

The Secret Life of the Home, 1972-221

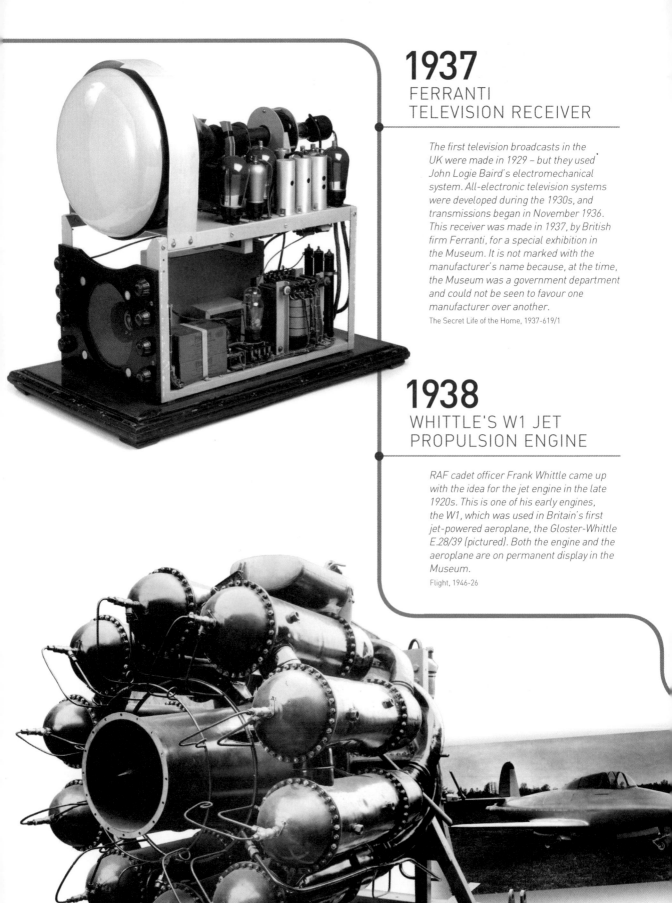

1937
FERRANTI
TELEVISION RECEIVER

The first television broadcasts in the UK were made in 1929 – but they used John Logie Baird's electromechanical system. All-electronic television systems were developed during the 1930s, and transmissions began in November 1936. This receiver was made in 1937, by British firm Ferranti, for a special exhibition in the Museum. It is not marked with the manufacturer's name because, at the time, the Museum was a government department and could not be seen to favour one manufacturer over another.

The Secret Life of the Home, 1937-619/1

1938
WHITTLE'S W1 JET
PROPULSION ENGINE

RAF cadet officer Frank Whittle came up with the idea for the jet engine in the late 1920s. This is one of his early engines, the W1, which was used in Britain's first jet-powered aeroplane, the Gloster-Whittle E.28/39 (pictured). Both the engine and the aeroplane are on permanent display in the Museum.

Flight, 1946-26

1945
BOWL FROM HIROSHIMA

The atomic bomb that was detonated
over the Japanese city of Hiroshima
killed almost 80,000 people directly; the
radioactive contamination it left behind
killed an estimated 60,000 more. This
porcelain bowl was found among the ruins
of the city (pictured). As a result of the heat
of the explosion, the glaze melted and sand
and stones became embedded in it.

Making the Modern World, 1984-663

1942
V2 ROCKET
GUIDANCE COMPONENTS

This pair of gyroscopes was part of the
stability and guidance unit of the German V2
rocket, the world's first long-range missile.
During 1944 and 1945, more than 3000 of
these weapons, each carrying 1 tonne of
high explosive, fell on London, southern
England and cities on mainland Europe.

Exploring Space, 1982-1264

1940s
PEDOSCOPE
X-RAY APPARATUS

This machine presented a picture of the bones in your foot and an outline of your shoes. Although there was little evidence to suggest that these devices would help you find perfectly fitting shoes, they were a fairly common sight in shoe shops from the 1930s to the 1960s. Their use quickly declined after scientists began to understand the risks associated with excessive exposure to X-rays.

Blythe House store, 1985-774

1945

MOLECULAR MODEL
OF PENICILLIN BY
DOROTHY HODGKIN

In the early 1940s, the antibiotic penicillin (see page 65) was hailed a wonder drug, after successful trials and its use on injured soldiers. In 1945, British chemist Dorothy Crowfoot Hodgkin used X-ray crystallography to work out its molecular structure. Her work enabled scientists to develop new antibiotics to treat infections.

Making the Modern World, 1996-686

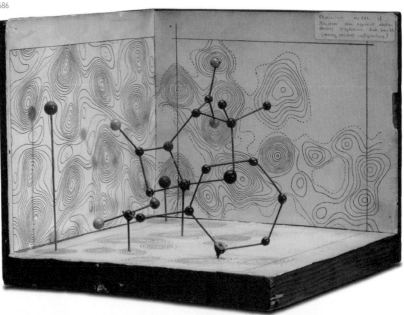

1948
X-RAY BUS

After the Second World War, the newly created National Health Service commissioned a fleet of 52 mobile X-ray vans as part of its effort to eradicate tuberculosis (TB). The vans travelled around Britain carrying out chest X-rays – as many as 120 per hour – to identify people with early signs of the disease. This X-ray bus is in storage, but you can take a virtual tour of it on our Brought to Life *website.*
Wroughton stores, 1979-62

1948
PRILECT ELECTRIC TRAVELLING IRON

If you ever wanted evidence of the influence of science and technology on culture, look no further than this picture. This simple travel iron was made possible by so many advances – including the development of stainless steel, synthetic materials and electricity supplies; and a growing demand for portable appliances prompted by mass transport and the 'golden age of travel'.
The Secret Life of the Home, 1979-62

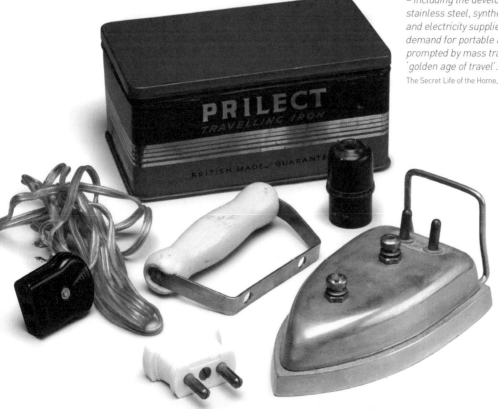

1949
WILLIAMSON'S HOME-CONSTRUCTED AMPLIFIER

In 1948, vinyl replaced shellac for making gramophone discs, bringing near-silent sound reproduction. As a result, audio buffs needed better-quality amplifiers. This high-fidelity amplifier was designed by British electronics engineer Theo Williamson. Instructions on how to build it appeared in the technical magazine Wireless World.
Blythe House store, 1982-1556

1950
IRON LUNG

Iron lungs were invented in the late 1920s and remained essential life-saving devices during the polio epidemics of the 1950s for patients who developed life-threatening paralysis and were unable to breathe. The iron lung was a negative pressure ventilator. The patient was placed in the sealed chamber (with their head sticking out of the large hole at the end) which was connected to an air pump that repeatedly changed the pressure inside the chamber, so that the person's lungs would compress and expand, letting them breathe until their nerves recovered.
Blythe House store, 1982-1449

1950
PILOT ACE

*In 1945, while working at the National Physical
Laboratory, British mathematician Alan
Turing formulated the design of an 'automatic
computing engine' (ACE), which would have
been the world's first general-purpose
computer. But Turing left the NPL in 1948. This
smaller 'pilot', or prototype, was made in his
absence in 1950. Although just a pilot' version,
this remarkable machine found a range of
applications, including working out the stresses
on an aeroplane's fuselage.*

Making the Modern World, 1956-152

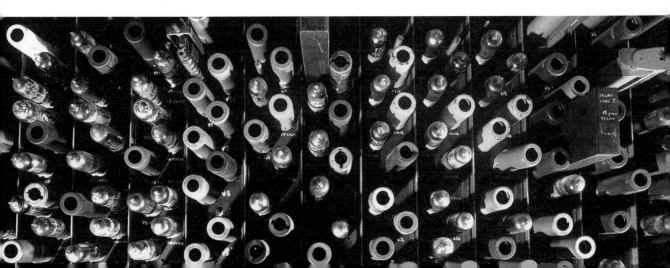

1953
CRICK AND WATSON'S DNA MODEL

In 1953, British and American molecular biologists
Francis Crick and James Watson pulled off one of
the most profound scientific triumphs of the century.
Using their knowledge of chemical bonds, along with
X-ray crystallography results from British chemist
Rosalind Franklin, they worked out the double helix
structure of DNA (deoxyribonucleic acid), the molecule
that acts as a blueprint for all living things and is
responsible for inherited characteristics. Within a
decade, scientists had worked out how information
is coded along the molecule. This reconstruction
of Watson and Crick's model includes some of the
original metal plates they used.

Making the Modern World, 1977-300

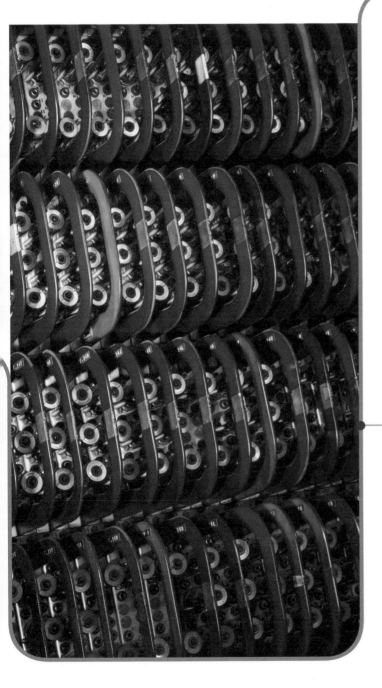

1959
MODEL OF NS *SAVANNAH* NUCLEAR-POWERED MERCHANT CARGO SHIP

The Nuclear Ship Savannah *was the first of only four nuclear-powered cargo ships ever built. A nuclear reactor on board heated water to produce steam, which turned a turbine (see page 54). The ship was in service until 1972. Although it ran well, it was more expensive to run than diesel-powered ships, which were the norm by then.*
Blythe House store, 1965-459/1

1959
FERRANTI PEGASUS COMPUTER

The Pegasus Computer was designed and built in the UK by Ferranti Ltd. Forty of these machines were built and put to work in banks, universities and engineering and research establishments. For most of these organisations and their staff, Pegasus was their first computer and therefore the herald of a new age.
Computing, 1983-1440

1959
MORRIS MINI-MINOR

This full-size cutaway Mini from 1959 shows just how successful Greek-British designer Alec Issigonis was in making this small car feel so spacious inside. The Mini was enormously successful: this is one of more than 5 million made altogether.

Making the Modern World, 1962-192/1

1959
ORAMICS MACHINE

Influential British musician Daphne Oram was one of the pioneers of electronic music, and a co-founder of the BBC Radiophonic Workshop. Her Oramics machine created sounds to order, being fed waveforms that were drawn on 35 mm film (below). Ten strips of film could be 'played' simultaneously.

Oramics to Electronica: Revealing Histories of Electronic Music, 2010-68

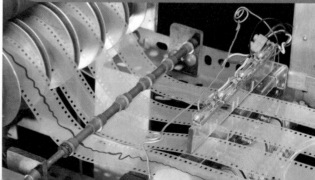

1960
'FOREST OF RODS'

British crystallographer John Kendrew and Austrian-British molecular biologist Max Perutz built this remarkable model, using steel rods in a wooden baseboard, to represent the molecular structure of myoglobin, a compound that stores oxygen in muscles. The two scientists won the 1962 Nobel Prize in Chemistry for their work determining the structure of this and other globular proteins.

Wroughton and Blythe House stores, 1977-219

1960

BLUE STEEL MISSILE

The Blue Steel air-launched supersonic 'stand-off bomb' was designed as an interim nuclear weapon before the proposed Blue Streak ballistic missile system. Blue Steel became operational in 1963 and was carried by Vulcan and Victor aircraft. It remained in operation for longer than intended, because Blue Streak was cancelled. It was retired in 1970, when the Polaris submarine-launched missile fleet came into service.

Wroughton stores, 1987-752

1964

PAIR OF CO_2-POWERED UPPER LIMB PROSTHESES

Starting in the 1950s – long before the computer-controlled neural interfaces and electric 'muscles' found in cutting-edge prostheses of today – prosthetic limb designers used pressurised carbon dioxide gas to offer some power and control. These arms were made for a 12-year-old boy who had lost his arms when he was eight. Notice how the shoulder fittings are soft, to allow for the child's growth.

Blythe House store, 1999-579

1965
STEEL MOULD FOR
TUPPERWARE CONTAINER

During the Second World War, British invention polythene was used extensively for military purposes. After 1945, it found various other applications, including the development of Tupperware – a range of kitchen containers featuring a patented seal – by American engineer Earl Silas Tupper. Tupperware became enormously popular after Tupper's marketing genius Brownie Wise developed the idea of 'party plan' selling.

Wroughton stores, 1985-201

1969
GREENWICH MEAN
TIME EQUIPMENT

Ever since 1924, the BBC has been broadcasting six short musical notes nicknamed 'the pips' to act as a time check on the hour. From 1970 they were provided by this equipment, installed at the Royal Greenwich Observatory in Sussex. It contained an atomic clock and sent signals along two telephone lines to Broadcasting House in London. It was retired in 1990, when the BBC began using its own atomic clock, as well as synchronising with other atomic clocks via radio links.

Making the Modern World, 1990-303

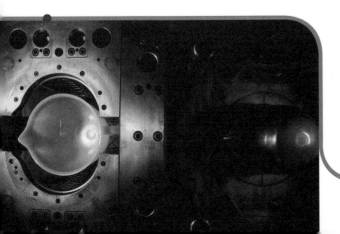

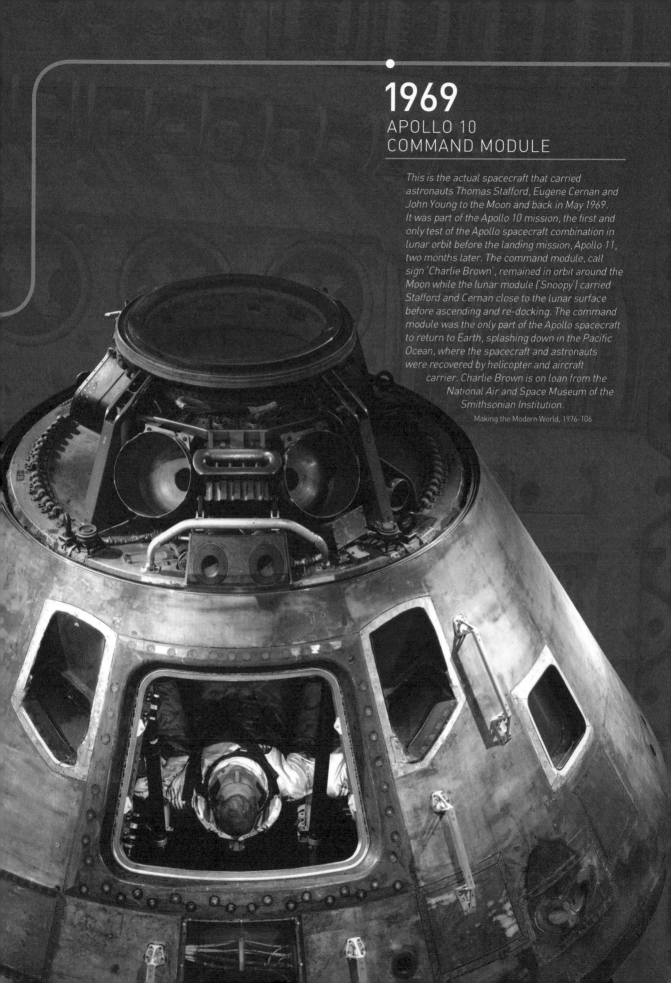

1969
APOLLO 10
COMMAND MODULE

This is the actual spacecraft that carried astronauts Thomas Stafford, Eugene Cernan and John Young to the Moon and back in May 1969. It was part of the Apollo 10 mission, the first and only test of the Apollo spacecraft combination in lunar orbit before the landing mission, Apollo 11, two months later. The command module, call sign 'Charlie Brown', remained in orbit around the Moon while the lunar module ('Snoopy') carried Stafford and Cernan close to the lunar surface before ascending and re-docking. The command module was the only part of the Apollo spacecraft to return to Earth, splashing down in the Pacific Ocean, where the spacecraft and astronauts were recovered by helicopter and aircraft carrier. Charlie Brown is on loan from the National Air and Space Museum of the Smithsonian Institution.

Making the Modern World, 1976-106

1970
VCS3 MUSIC SYNTHESISER

Music synthesisers became commercially available in the mid 1960s. Early models were all very large and very expensive. The VCS3 – a modular analogue synthesiser made by British company Electronic Music Studios – was practically portable and much more affordable. Many pioneers of electronic music in the 1970s used the VCS3, including Pink Floyd and Roxy Music.

Oramics to Electronica: Revealing Histories of Electronic Music, 1970-318

1970s
MITRAL AND AORTIC REPLACEMENT HEART VALVES

Valvular stenosis is a condition in which one or more valves in the heart do not open fully, restricting normal blood flow and putting extra strain on the heart. Artificial valves like these (shown here standing on tubes for display) dramatically improve sufferers' survival rates. The first implant of an artificial valve was performed in 1952, but these are from the 1970s.

Who am I?, A600965

1970
BOEING 747

Even in our large objects store in Wroughton (see page 15), we don't really have enough room for a complete Boeing 747. We do, however, have this section of a Boeing 747SP fuselage – featuring the cargo hold and two floors of seating – on display in Flight on the third floor. The 'SP' variation (for 'Special Performance') entered service in 1976. The Boeing 747, nicknamed the 'Jumbo Jet', revolutionised passenger air travel after it was introduced in 1970. Its large size dramatically lowered operating costs per passenger journey, making long-haul flights affordable for many more people.
Flight, 1992-823

1971
BLACK ARROW
R4 LAUNCH VEHICLE

This British Black Arrow R4 rocket would have launched the Miranda satellite in 1974. However, Black Arrow was cancelled, Miranda was launched by a US rocket and R4 was presented to the Science Museum. Its predecessor, R3, made history on 28 October 1971 by being the first and, to date, only British rocket to launch a British satellite... which will continue to orbit Earth for the rest of this century.

Exploring Space, 1972-325

1973
SINCLAIR CAMBRIDGE
POCKET CALCULATOR

The development of integrated circuits in the 1960s made it possible for manufacturers to cram all the components needed for an electronic calculator on to a single chip of silicon. As a result battery-powered pocket-sized calculators became a reality in the 1970s. This one, made by British company Sinclair Radionics, sold for £43.95 when it was released – equivalent to around £480 today.

Blythe House store, 1974-505

1984
PHILIPS
COMPACT DISC PLAYER

The compact disc (CD) was developed in a collaboration between Japanese company Sony and Dutch company Philips. The first CD player, Sony's CDP-101, was launched on 1 October 1982. Shown here is one of Philips' early offerings, from 1984: the CD100, which was the first top-loading CD player.

The Secret Life of the Home, 1994-187

1984
APPLE MACINTOSH COMPUTER

Apple Computer Inc. designed the Apple Macintosh to be as user-friendly as possible. It had a 23 cm (9-inch) monochrome monitor screen, 128 kilobytes of RAM, and came with a keyboard and mouse, a novelty for the time. It was the first personal computer with a graphical user interface (GUI) – featuring a 'desktop', windows and clickable menus, rather than a text-based display. Within a year, Microsoft introduced its own GUI operating system, Windows.
Blythe House store, 1993-1089

1984
'JEDI' HELMET

MRI (magnetic resonance imaging) was new and experimental during the 1980s. Having a scan could prove intimidating, especially for children. To produce clear images of the head, copper coils had to be placed close to the head, to increase magnetic sensitivity. Ian Young, at Hammersmith Hospital, made the experience less daunting by incorporating the coils into helmets reminiscent of those used by trainee Jedi knights in the Star Wars films.
Health Matters *and* Who am I?, 1993-1003

1985
VODAFONE TRANSPORTABLE MOBILE PHONE

Vodafone launched the UK's first 'cellular' mobile phone network on 1 January 1985. This early mobile phone would normally remain in a user's car, but could be lifted out and carried round – although it only offered a few minutes of call time before the battery went flat. Battery technology has moved on since then – and network cells are smaller, so less power is needed to communicate with a base station.

Blythe House store, 1997-1038

1985
SPACELAB 2 X-RAY TELESCOPE

This telescope, designed and built at Birmingham University, used a gold-plated 'mask' to create images of X-rays from distant objects in space (conventional lenses can't focus X-rays). It formed part of the Spacelab 2 mission carried into space in July 1985 aboard Space Shuttle Challenger. From its position above the atmosphere, the telescope returned many days' worth of new data including the first high-energy X-ray images of our own galaxy's centre.

Wroughton Stores, 2005-33

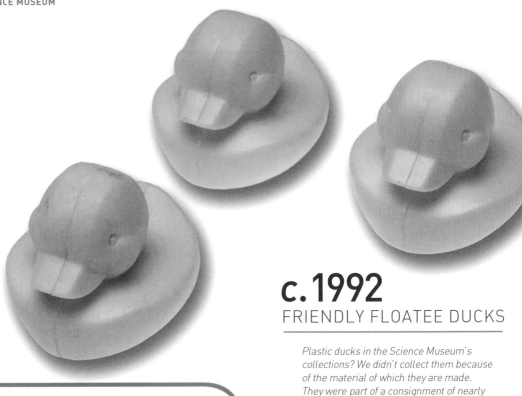

c.1992
FRIENDLY FLOATEE DUCKS

Plastic ducks in the Science Museum's collections? We didn't collect them because of the material of which they are made. They were part of a consignment of nearly 30,000 plastic toys that fell into the north Pacific from a container ship in 1992. Many of those toys inadvertently became part of a massive scientific study: beachcombers have been finding them ever since, helping oceanographers refine their models of ocean surface currents.

Blythe House store, 2005-393

1988
ONCOMOUSE

On 12 April 1988, the US Patent and Trademark Office issued the world's first patent on an animal. The subject of the patent was the Harvard Mouse, or OncoMouse – a strain of mice created by inserting a gene from a virus into the DNA of mouse embryos. The resulting mice and their progeny were used in cancer research, because they were much more susceptible to cancer than normal mice. The very first transgenic animal was also a mouse, again created with virus DNA, in 1974.

Making the Modern World, 1989-437

1990s
PROTOTYPE GYROSCOPE FOR GRAVITY PROBE B

Gravity Probe B was an experiment staged in orbit in 2004–05. It was the most precise test to date of Einstein's general theory of relativity – specifically, whether the Earth warps its local space-time. The experiment was based on four rapidly spinning gyroscopes whose orientation against a guide star was monitored. Each gyroscope contained a ball made of fused quartz, coated with a thin layer of niobium. At the time, the balls were the most perfect spheres ever manufactured.
Cosmos & Culture, 2005-75

1990s
TRACY THE SHEEP

You've probably heard of Dolly the sheep – but have you heard of Tracy? Tracy was a transgenic sheep born in Scotland in 1990. She was created to carry a gene that would produce a protein in her milk called human alpha-1 antitrypsin, which was considered a promising treatment for cystic fibrosis and some cases of the lung disease emphysema.
Making the Modern World, 1999 97

2009
PROTOTYPE
90-CHANNEL MRI CAP

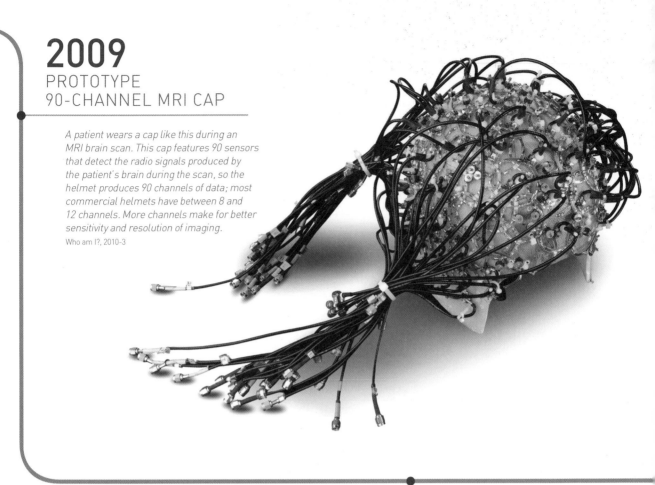

A patient wears a cap like this during an MRI brain scan. This cap features 90 sensors that detect the radio signals produced by the patient's brain during the scan, so the helmet produces 90 channels of data; most commercial helmets have between 8 and 12 channels. More channels make for better sensitivity and resolution of imaging.

Who am I?, 2010-3

2010
PORTRAIT OF JAMES WATT

When preparing James Watt's workshop for relocation to its current home on the ground floor (see page 90), curators examined several plaster moulds. Among representations of animals and mythological gods, they found this one they thought might be a bust of Watt himself. Laser scanning and computer analysis by the 3D Imaging Research Centre at University College, London, allowed the bust to be recreated for the first time in more than 200 years.

James Watt and Our World, 2011-14

2010
MOBILE PHONE BOX
FROM CAMEROON

On a visit to Cameroon in 2012, Museum staff purchased this colourful roadside booth, where small businessman Emmanuel Bongsunu sold mobile phone credit and accessories. The purchase enabled Bongsunu to buy a new booth – and the Museum to acquire an artefact that will inform visitors about the rise and importance of mobile technology in Africa.

Information Age, E2012.131.1

2010
COVAFLU FFP3 DISPOSABLE
FACE MASK

Face masks like this one are a familiar sight in news stories about flu pandemics. Modern face masks are made to high precision; this one filters out any particles larger than 0.3 microns (0.0003 mm) in diameter, which includes nearly all airborne droplets produced by sneezing. Made by British company Clinova, this mask is held at the Museum's Blythe House store for small and medium-sized objects.

Blythe House store, 2012-74

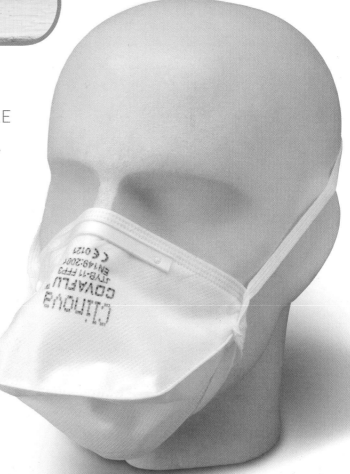

SCIENCE
AND
CULTURE

Science and technology are as much a part of culture as art, music or literature, or, indeed, as much as Facebook and television. We remember that in everything we do – from choosing what to collect and exhibit to how we present contemporary issues in science.

BELOW
Electroboutique Pop-up, *a contemporary arts project part-commissioned by the Museum and funded by Arts Council England, and made by art production company Electroboutique (Russian artists Alexei Shulgin and Aristarkh Chernyshev).*

DRIVERS OF CULTURE

Electronic circuits, electric light, plastics, bicycles and space rockets are just as much the result of human ingenuity as are great works of art, literature or music. And just like the arts, these products of scientific and technological endeavour reflect who we are and what we strive for. But science and technology don't just reflect culture, they help to define and redefine it. The discoveries of science shape our understanding of the world, and permeate our beliefs, our prejudices and our attitudes. Meanwhile, new technologies – such as labour-saving domestic appliances or new means of communication or transport – profoundly change our behaviours and habits.

As you wander the Museum's galleries, evidence of the role of science and technology in creating culture is all around you – as is evidence of our efforts to make sense of it. Innovations and scientific discoveries continue to affect the way we live, and understanding them makes us more prepared for the future; that is why we put so much emphasis on important issues in contemporary science, such as genetics, robotics and climate change.

REVOLUTIONS

TOP
Fish-eye panoramic view of James Watt's workshop, the centrepiece of James Watt and Our World on the ground floor.

RIGHT
Plate taken from a late-19th-century manual for engineers showing a condensing beam engine made by James Watt & Co.

BELOW
Another panoramic view of Watt's workshop.

Many of our most prized objects date from the Industrial Revolution – a time when technology began rapidly changing the lives of millions of ordinary people. It started in Britain during the 18th century, with the rise of factories powered first by water wheels and then steam engines. Steel, concrete and textiles became cheap and abundant, and brought wealth and power to Britain. The landscape changed too, as people flocked from the country to the cities to work in the factories.

On the ground floor of the Science Museum is *James Watt and Our World* – a shrine to one of the key players in the Industrial Revolution. The centrepiece of the exhibition is Watt's workshop – the furniture, floorboards, door and window, and more than 8000 objects preserved in exactly the state Watt left them when he died in 1819. The workshop is a time capsule of the man himself – there are chemistry experiments, tools, drawings, letters and sculptures, and an array of objects put aside in case they might have come in useful – reminding us that behind every scientific or technological development are human beings. It is also a cultural time capsule – of the new industrial era in which Watt was working, which he and his fellow engineers helped to define. When the contents of the workshop were moved to the Museum in 1924, the curators were even offered the dust from the room – such was the importance of this man, and the time in which he lived, in shaping the modern world.

In the second half of the 19th century and the early 20th century – a period often referred to as the Second Industrial Revolution – electricity, the internal combustion engine and the chemical industry were the main drivers of technological change. The telephone, the motorcar, television, recorded sound, calculating machines and computers, synthetic pigments and new materials – all of these have underpinned huge changes in the way the world looks and how we experience it.

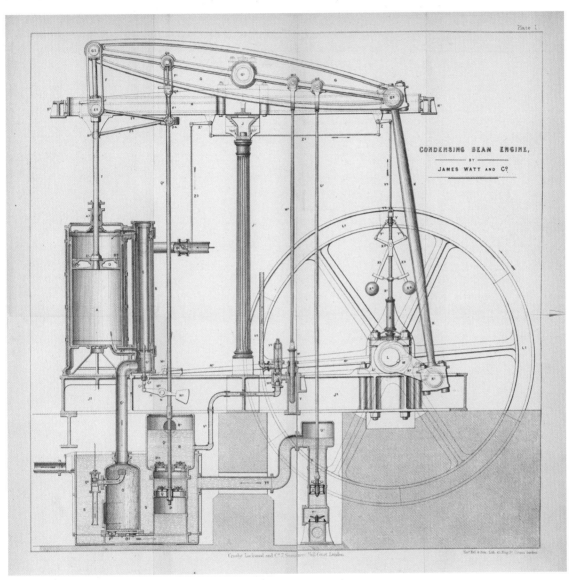

Plate 1.

CONDENSING BEAM ENGINE,
BY
JAMES WATT AND C?

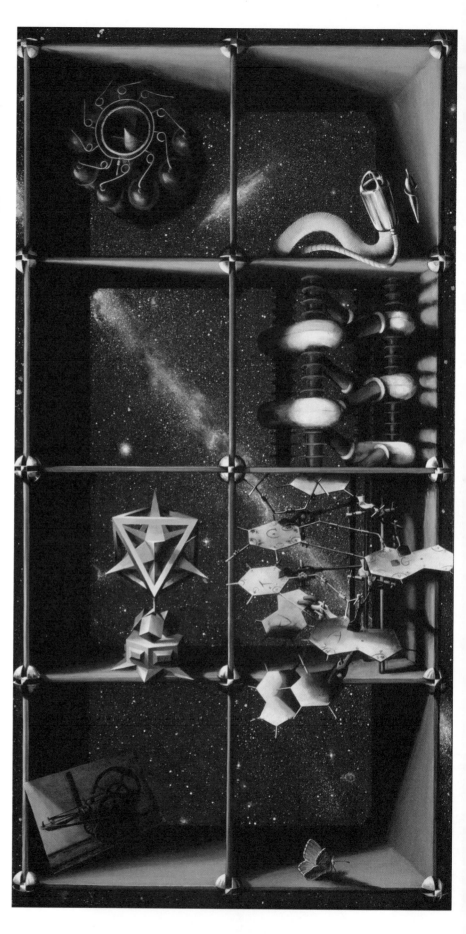

RIGHT

Serendip, *the central panel of a triptych that highlights some of the Museum's most prized objects. Created by Keith Holmes, the Museum's Artist in Residence from 1994 to 1996.*

ART AND PHOTOGRAPHY AT THE SCIENCE MUSEUM

The Science Museum has always collected and commissioned fine and contemporary art. Our fine art collection contains over 8000 works relating to the history of science, technology and medicine, including more than 80 portraits. The Science Museum Group also holds the National Photography Collection – a unique record of aesthetic, conceptual and technological developments in photography, from the earliest experiments to the latest digital techniques, and probably the world's finest collection of early photographs. Among its images and objects are entire collections, including the Daily Herald Archive, the Royal Photographic Society Collection and the Kodak Museum Collection. Media Space, on the second floor, invites contemporary photographers, artists, curators and practitioners from the creative industries to draw on the National Photography Collection, the broader collections of the Science Museum Group and the visual media in general. This new venture is a collaboration between the Science Museum and one of the other museums in the Science Museum Group – the National Media Museum, in Bradford – and features permanent photography and arts galleries as well as world-class exhibitions, talks and events.

BELOW
The most famous of the paintings we hold, Coalbrookdale by Night *is an 1801 work by Philip James de Loutherbourg that depicts the drama of pouring iron from a blast furnace at Bedlam, near Coalbrookdale, Shropshire.*

Media Space builds on the work of our Contemporary Arts Programme, launched in 1995, which commissions and purchases works from artists in all media – from painting, sculpture and photography to software, hardware and performance. The resulting works bring new, thought-provoking perspectives on the past, present and future of science and technology and their impact on society. A Cockroach Tour of the Science Museum, for example, is a participatory arts project created by Danish artists' collective Superflex. It is a chance to reflect on humans' technological progress – and their preoccupation with 'speed, time and burning things' – through the eyes of one of the planet's true survivors, the cockroach. Participants wear cockroach costumes and wander the Museum's galleries, becoming part of the artwork themselves, both observing and being observed by other visitors.

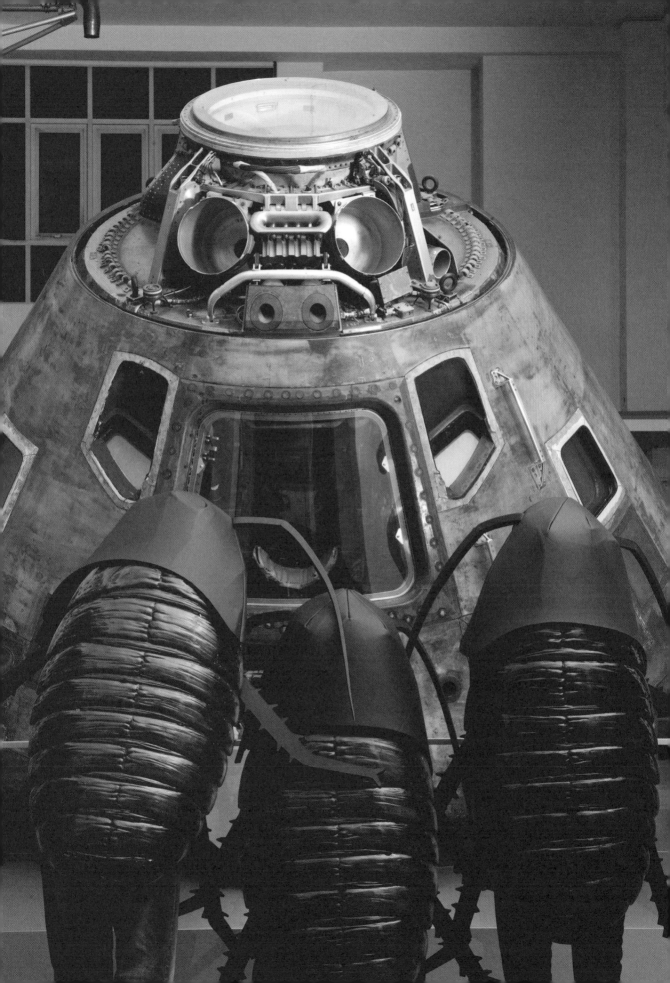

Inspire the great minds of tomorrow

To continue to inspire the great minds of the future, we need your support. Show your support by making a donation today, joining us as a Patron or becoming a volunteer – and help us make a difference, together.

Thank you for your donation

We would like to thank all our visitors, who have shown tremendous generosity by donating on their visits to us. We are now raising almost £1 million a year in visitor donations.

Become a Patron – invest in our future

If you share our passion, join us by becoming a Patron of the Science Museum. Your support will help us develop inspirational education programmes, protect our exceptional collections and refresh our world-renowned galleries. You will receive a tailored programme of special events designed to bring you closer to the heart of the Museum.

A gift in your will – a lasting legacy

Leaving a gift in your will to the Science Museum is the most personal, precious and lasting contribution anyone can make. Any gift, large or small, will help to ensure that the Museum can educate and delight visitors for generations to come.

Get involved – become a Science Museum volunteer

Investing your time and energy is very important to us and we welcome all to our volunteering programme, whatever your background or experience. Volunteers help out in all areas of the Museum, gaining invaluable hands-on experience, and are critical to ensuring we can offer the most to our visitors. Contact us at volunteer@sciencemuseum.ac.uk.

If you would like further information about supporting the Science Museum, please visit www.sciencemuseum.org.uk/supportus or contact us directly at development@sciencemuseum.ac.uk.

We are grateful for the support from all of our funders including:

Accenture
ARM Holdings plc
Bank of America Merrill Lynch
Barclays Group
Bayer plc
BG Group plc
BP
Broccoli Foundation
BT Group plc
Cambridge Wireless
The DCMS/Wolfson Museums & Galleries Improvement Fund
Department of Environment, Food and Rural Affairs

EADS
The Garfield Weston Foundation
GlaxoSmithKline
Google
Heritage Lottery Fund
Hyundai Motor UK
The Institution of Engineering and Technology
The Kusuma Trust UK
Life Technologies Foundation
MasterCard
Michael and Jane Wilson
Motorola Solutions Foundation
The Pilgrim Trust

Qualcomm
Rentokil-Initial plc
Science Museum Acquisition Donors
Science Museum Exhibition Donors
Science Museum Patrons
Shell International
Siemens plc
Virgin Media
Wellcome Trust
The Wolfson Foundation

The Science Museum would like to thank the following sources for their kind permission to reproduce some of the images in this book. The illustrations on page 5 taken from 'Science Museum Conservation Plan' by Alan Baxter, reproduced courtesy of the Survey of London; the Wells Cathedral clock on page 36 reproduced courtesy of the Dean and Chapter of Wells Cathedral; William Herschel's telescope on page 42 reproduced courtesy of the Royal Astronomical Society; the Cooke and Wheatstone five-needle telegraph on page 46 is on loan from King's College London; Joseph John Thomson's cathode ray tube on page 54 reproduced courtesy of Cavendish Laboratory, Cambridge; the V2 rocket guidance components on page 67 are on loan from Cranfield University; the Apollo 10 command module on page 78 is on loan from the Smithsonian National Air and Space Museum, Washington, DC; the MRI cap on page 86 reproduced courtesy of A A Martinos, Center for Biological Imaging of the Massachusetts General Hospital; the portrait of James Watt on page 86 reproduced courtesy of UCL Digital Manufacturing Centre; the Covaflu™ FFP3 on page 87 reproduced courtesy of Clinova Ltd; the mobile phone box on page 87 © Sjoerd Epe Sijsma; *The Munitions Girls* on page 89 © the estate of Stanhope Alexander Forbes/Bridgeman Art Library; *Serendip* on page 92 © Keith Holmes; *Renewable Energy* on page 94 © The estate of Phillip Fooks. Images on the front and back cover and pages 1, 4, 6, 7, 8, 9, 10, 11, 12, 13, 14, 15, 16, 17, 18, 19, 20, 21, 22, 23, 24, 25, 26, 27, 28, 29, 30, 31, 32, 33, 34, 35, 36 (tl &b), 37, 38, 39, 40, 41, 42 (t & b), 43, 44, 45, 46, 47, 48, 49, 50, 51, 52, 53, 54 (tl & tr), 55, 56, 57, 58, 59, 60, 61, 62, 63, 64, 65, 66, 67, 68, 69, 70, 71, 72, 73, 74, 75, 76, 77, 78, 79, 80, 81, 82, 83, 84, 85, 86 (b), 88, 90-91, 93, 94 (t), 95 © Science & Society Picture Library (SSPL). Every effort has been made to acknowledge correctly and contact the source and/or copyright holder of the images in this book and SCMG Enterprises Ltd apologises for any unintentional errors or omissions, which will be corrected in future editions of the book.